The author is the youngest child of Sam and Kate Robinson. He was born in 1944 and left school at 14 years old. He worked in England as a messenger boy in a theatrical agent's office in 1959. Then he returned to Dublin in 1960 and started an apprenticeship as a plasterer. From there, he emigrated to Canada as a plasterer in 1966 lived and worked in Toronto in construction. He married Florence in Canada in 1967. He is now retired and has been living back in Dublin with Florence since 2006.

To Sam and Kate Robinson who through trying and difficult times managed to raise a large and happy family. Thank you.

Eamonn Robinson

THE SEED OF FREEDOM

AUSTIN MACAULEY PUBLISHERS™

LONDON • CAMBRIDGE • NEW YORK • SHARJAH

A CIP catalogue record for this title is available from the British Library.

ISBN 9781398486591 (Paperback)
ISBN 9781398486607 (ePub e-book)

www.austinmacauley.com

First Published 2023
Austin Macauley Publishers Ltd®
1 Canada Square
Canary Wharf
London
E14 5AA

Thanks to my wife Florence who helped me, and Paddy Rowan who encouraged me to write the story. Thanks to the Custom House family group. Des White for all your fascinating research.

Introduction

My name is Jeremiah Robinson, although no one calls me that. They call me Sam, a nickname I picked up playing football that stuck with me most of my life. I am 11 almost 12 years old at this time in 1916, Dublin. We live in the market area in East Arran Street on the north side, off the Quays near the city centre. This is a story of boy's growing into young men in what was the most important and tumultuous time in modern Irish history.

Book 1

Chapter 1
Beginning

We are the Robinson family, there are four of us, my Mam, Molly, Christy and me. My sister Molly is the oldest, she is almost 16, Christy is almost 14 and I am 11. My Mam is Elizabeth, known as "Lizzy Kennedy", her maiden name. Mam is a fish dealer in the market, where she sells fish as her mother did before her.

I didn't know my dad, he died when I was just a baby. He was from a sporting family and had been playing handball in the hand ball alley in Green St, after a game he lay down on the grass in the park and caught a cold which became pneumonia and he died he was only 23 years old. I was only 6 months old. So, my mother had to raise us on her own with the help of her relatives and family.

Because Mam worked, her sister Dinah who was a spinster lived with us and looked after the house and us. When I say house, it was a flat with two rooms and a scullery for preparing food. There were four flats with a big entrance where there were four doors in an enclosure facing the street. There was a toilet outside in the yard. Compared with a lot of the houses in the area around us, this was luxury. We were on street level and had running water in the kitchen. A lot of the area where we lived were tenement houses with 8 or 10 families living in one house with no running water.

My Mam's uncle Jerry lived beside us and her cousins lived next door. The whole clan lived within 100 yards of us. They were a very close-knit group whose history in the fish market goes back generations. My Mam worked very hard and was an astute and successful businesswoman.

As I mentioned, Molly was the oldest and was now helping in the market with Mam. Christy was at secondary school, and I was in my last year at Strand Street Primary School. It was the spring of 1916, and the first world war was raging. A lot of Irish men had joined up to fight, some hoping that it might lead to Home Rule in Ireland, but mostly they joined as a means of supporting their families. There was not a lot of work for ordinary people, especially the poor and uneducated, so the men went to war. There were also the Irish Volunteers who originally were formed because the Protestant people in the North had formed an Army of Volunteers to fight in France which now supported a Unionist movement in the North of Ireland. They wanted their own country. Then there was the Citizen Army formed by the Trade Union's in Dublin by James Connolly, to protect the workers after the General Strike in 1913. Where the people were killed by the Army on Bachelor's Walk for protesting. So, soldiers in uniform of all description were a common sight, some of the men on our street were members. Kids just do what kids do and so we lived in this situation without thinking too much about it.

One Saturday morning as usual, we were knocking the ball around the street with our pals, when I say ball, it is an exaggeration, it was a ball made with rags tied with string. The street was busy with horse and carts and hand carts, so Christy said, "Let's go down to the Square, there's more room."

"OK, let's go," I said. We go down to Ormond Square which has a wide patch in the middle. There's already some lads having a kickabout, we know most of them.

Christy, who is our leader, goes to Dickie who's the main fella with their lads, "Do you want to have a game, lads?"

"Yeah ok, but you have more players than us."

"OK," Christy said, "you can have Sam."

"Why do I always have to go on the other team?" I asked.

"Never mind, do you want a game or not?" Christy said.

"All right," I said. So, we set up to play. Christy was a very talented footballer and so was Dickie, they were the ones that scored most of the goals. I usually played back. Although Christy was older than me, I was almost as big, and I was good at stopping the forwards. We made up goals and started playing. During the game Christy gets a ball, sidesteps a defender and just as he goes to shoot, I tackle him and take away his shot. He goes flying and gets up screaming at me.

"What did you do that for?"

I said, "My job, you gave me to the other team." He just laughed, and we got on with the game. Playing football was our way of escape. As I went to head a ball I jumped up and landed awkwardly and fell, cutting my shin on a brick. I didn't take much notice of it, just carried on. Football took us out of the present and gave us a sense of freedom. We didn't bother to keep score, just had fun.

On Saturday Mam only worked a half day and we had to go over to help her clean and stack the fish boxes on the hand cart to get the fish in Howth the following week. As we finished, we noticed this man had been watching us. He came over and started talking to us. He asked, "How would you lads like to play on a proper team?"

"What do you mean?" We asked.

"I mean play on a proper pitch with a real ball."

"We would love that," I said.

"Well If you like, you can try out for our team. I'm the trainer," he said.

Christy asked, "Where do you play?"

He said, "up in the Park on Saturday or Sunday afternoons."

"We would be able to go then, we will have to ask our Mam," we said.

"What's the name of the team I asked?"

"Parade Rovers, we are over in Church Street at the hall. My name is John Molloy. Ask yer Da and see what he said."

"We don't have a Da," I said.

"Sorry I didn't know. Anyway, see what your Ma said so." Off we went to do our job for Mam.

When we got to the market the women were having their tea and chat getting ready to head home. Christy and I got stuck in to washing out the boxes with the hose and stacking them up on the hand cart. After about an hour or so we were nearly finished, and it was our turn for a cuppa. As we sat down for our tea Annie, one of the market women, said to me "What happened your leg?"

"I fell playing football," I answered. There was blood on my stocking, and it had dried and stuck to my leg.

"You better put something on that leg, it could get infected," she said. "Just a minute I have some ointment in my bag for emergencies." With that she took out a little tin of Zambuk ointment and got some water, washed my leg and applied the ointment. "Now, isn't that better?" She asked.

"Yes! Thank you, that's great." This was the start of my use of Zambuk ointment, from which I would get my nick name "Sam."

One of the women had some lovely fresh cream buns from the bakery in Abbey St We were enjoying them when Christy asked "Hey Mam, did you know there was a football club in Church St?"

"No, I never heard anything about that."

"This man asked us if we wanted to join," I said. "What man?" Said Mam.

"He said his name was John Molloy from Church St."

Mary Ann, one of the other dealers, piped up, "I know him," she said, "they live on Church Parade."

"Yeah," Christy said, "the team is called Parade Rovers."

"They're a nice family," Mary Ann said. "John tries to help the young lads in the neighbourhood, he tries to keep them out of trouble."

Mam said, "Are you finished what you were doing?"

"Almost," said Christy, "be about 10 minutes."

"Well hurry yourselves and get home for your dinner. Dinah will have it ready."

We got on with our work and when we were done, we started home. I asked Christy, "Do you think Mam will let us join? I'd love to play on a proper pitch."

Mam came in just as dinner was ready. We were dying to ask her about the football team. I couldn't wait any longer and blurted out, "Can we join the football team, Mam?"

"Well now," Ma said, "we will have to see what's involved and when these games are played. I still need you to help me on Saturday and Mass on Sunday."

"Mr Molloy said they play on either Saturday or Sunday afternoon."

"Well, I suppose it would do you good to be out in the fresh air in the Park."

"Ah thanks Mam, that's great. We will go up to the club this afternoon and find out the story," said Christy. As soon as we wolfed down our dinner, we headed over to Church St to the hall where the club was supposed to be. There was no sign of Mr Molloy there. Another man was about to lock the door we asked, "Where's Mr Molloy?"

"He's gone up to the Park! With some of the boys for training. They only left half an hour ago, if you hurry, you'd catch up with them. They play over near the Monument," he told us.

Christy had tuppence in his pocket. "Come on we'll get a tram on the Quays." We ran down and just caught the tram at the end of Church St It only took 10 minutes, and we were at the park gates. I loved going on the Tram, upstairs you could see the river over the wall. We could see the Monument from the tram, you couldn't miss it, it's the biggest thing in the park, in honour of the Duke of Wellington. Apparently, he was born in Dublin but didn't think he was Irish.

Across the road we saw boys with blue shirts kicking ball, there were goal posts and Mr Molloy was with them. We ran over to him; he was delighted to see us. "That's great you came, you can have a kick around with us," he said, "Put on yer boots!"

"We don't have any boots yet, only our ordinary boots."

"Well as long as you don't mind slipping and sliding you can join in. We'll see how you do." He gave us a blue shirt each and we started training, kicking, running and heading the ball. The ball felt very heavy at first being made from leather. It took a while to get used to. After about an hour Mr Molloy split us up and we had a little game it was brilliant. We really enjoyed it and we were tired by the time we finished.

"OK lads," said Mr Molloy, "time to go. Next week we are having a proper game against another club so be here at 2 o'clock. We will see you all then. By the way from now on you can call me Coach! Mr Molloy was my Da." We all laughed. "You Robinson boy's, you have to have proper boots to play and nicks, maybe you can borrow some?"

When we got home, Molly was at the door. "My god," she said, "look at the cut of you two, you're filthy." She was right, we had been sliding and falling around in the grass. We never had so much fun.

"Dinah will murder you, she's going to have to wash out your clothes." Dinah did the washing; she wasn't too happy.

On Sunday after we had been to Mass and had dinner Uncle Jerry was taking us for a jaunt in his pony and trap to Dollymount beach. It was a lovely day, and we were looking forward to a day at the seaside. Uncle Jerry looked after us on account of not having a father. He was a great man for stories. He would tell us about ancient Ireland, Cú Chulainn, and the Red Branch Knight's. He used to say he would have been a Fenian if he had been born sooner. He made sure we went to school and helped my mother out as much as he could. He worked on the Barges, ferrying beer from the Guinness brewery to the ships at the Custom House Quay. He was also good for a penny now and then.

We told him about joining the football club, he was delighted. He said he might be able to borrow boots for us. It was beautiful day and a joy to be at the seaside. It was going to be a long week till Saturday and playing in a real match. The days dragged on and we hadn't heard from Uncle Jerry, so we were a bit disappointed. On the Friday when I got home from school there was a parcel in the front room on the table and Mam was sitting having a cup of tea with Aunt Dinah.

"So how did you get on today?" Mam said.

"OK," I said "was Uncle Jerry able to get the boots for us?" I asked.

"No," Mam said, "I never heard from him."

I was crushed, I was looking forward to playing. Ma said, "It's not easy to borrow stuff like that it costs a lot of money. It's Easter next week. You'll get an Easter egg."

"I'd rather have football boots." I said sulking away.

"Ahh well," said Mam, "we'll see."

"Where's Christy?" Dinah asked.

"I saw him talking to Mick Mulligan in the street, he should be in any minute" I said. With that Christy walks in. Mam was acting a bit little funny. Our mam was not what you would call "lovey dovey." I guess not having a husband made it hard for her. She was very practical, and she worked very hard; she is not usually so casual.

"What's in the parcel?" Christy asked spying it on the table.

"Oh that?" said Mam, "I picked it up at Millen's on my way home." Millen's was a sports shop on Mary St Me and Christy looked at each other.

"Is it for us?" I asked.

"Well, it's not for me," said Dinah smiling.

"Happy Easter," said Mam handing the brown package to us. We tore into the package, there were two pairs of football boots and two pairs of nicks inside. We were stunned.

"Thanks Mam," we both said. Mam wasn't the mushy type, she and Dinah just smiled, and she said, "Take care of them."

Dinah said, "it will save on the washing." I went over to Mam and gave her a hug. I just felt her hand rest on my head and ruffle my hair. "By the way, no Easter eggs this year," Dinah said with a laugh. We put our new boots and nicks on a shelf near our bed where we could keep an eye on them.

Christy and I couldn't wait for the game. We went to the Market earlier than usual so we would finish our job earlier. Never before had we finished our work so quickly. We both ate sparingly at our dinner. Ma and Dinah watched us and then said, "You might as well get going before you choke yourselves if you keep sitting there. I'll keep your dinner till you come home."

We grabbed our new gear and took off feeling very full of ourselves. Of course, we were the first ones there and got stripped off and into our boots and nicks. It felt great to have proper football boots on. When the coach Mr Molloy came he was pleased we had our gear. "You'll have to learn to look after your boots, you have to keep them clean and rub Dubbin on them to make them soft and waterproof."

He gave out the shirts. I got number 2 and Christy was given number 8. He told us I was right fullback and Christy was inside right. He gave us a ball to practice with while we were waiting. Dickie Giles also showed up for our team, he was left halfback.

The other team was Home Farm, a well-known team from Drumcondra. They had a good reputation. Once we were organised the game began. It took a while for me to get used to the grass and their forwards were very quick. Before long they were up a goal. You could see they were well used to playing together. As we were a new team we couldn't deal with their speed and by halftime we were 2 goals down. With Christy playing in front of me I tried to pass the ball down the wing.

The Coach encouraged us and told us not to be afraid to play our own game. We started to knock the ball around and made a few passes. As their winger came running down my side with the ball, just as he was ready to cross, I took a run and slid in to take the ball away. I got the ball, and he went flying. He wasn't too happy, called me a few names. I called him a few back. We got a few shots on them. Christy hit the post, the ball bounced out as Dickie was running in and he bashed it into the net.

We scored our first goal, close to the end of the game they scored again. So ended our first game. We thought it was awful to lose, but the coach was pleased. He said, "These lads have been together for a couple of years; it takes time for a team to play well together. We did OK, we scored a goal."

"Hey, Sam that was some sliding tackle! Be careful you don't hurt yourself." That was the first time I ever heard of a "sliding tackle." It was to become my signature move all through my playing career.

When we got home, Mam was anxious to hear how we made out, even Molly was interested. "How did it go?" She asked.

"We lost 3 to 1."

"Did you do your best?" Ma said.

"We sure did," said Christy "Sam almost put one of their players in the Liffey." Then he laughed.

"OK you two," said Ma, "it's Easter Sunday tomorrow so put your stuff away, and you have to get cleaned up and go to confession. It's on till 5 o'clock in Halston St." After we got home and had our tea we went outside into the street. It was a lovely evening, some of the women had brought out chairs and were sitting chatting and knitting. There seemed to be an undercurrent of anticipation in the air. There were rumours of Parades being cancelled and other goings on; being a kid I just forgot about it. It was a holiday weekend, there was racing at Fairyhouse and plans for a trip to the Strawberry Beds near Lucan with Uncle Jerry. That night I dreamt of playing football and winning cups.

The Sunday morning was beautiful, a warm day with lots of sunshine. Once mass and dinner were over Christy and me helped get the pony and trap ready. Then we all loaded on and set out for Lucan. Mam and Dinah had their best hats on as it was a holiday. I loved the clippety-clop sound the horse made on the cobblestones. There were lots of people out and about being such a nice day.

Going through the Park we saw a polo game going on, and there were loads of people at the Zoo. When we reached the Anglers Rest Pub along the river Liffey we stopped. We had a picnic with us and there was an area at the riverbank for picnics. The sun was shining, and spring was in the air, we sat on the grass. Uncle Jerry got a pint and a couple of bottles of stout for the women at the pub, we got orange squash and we ate our sandwiches. We watched some men on the other side of the river fishing. It felt good to be out in the fresh air having a good time. The day flew by leaving me with a feeling of happiness and warmth. Going to sleep that night little did we know what the following day would bring.

Chapter 2
Easter Rising

Easter Monday dawned a beautiful sunny morning. As it was a bank holiday, we were looking forward to having a kick about with our pals after our breakfast. We went out into the street, there seemed to be tension in the air. Some of the men that lived on the street were in their uniforms, the Irish Volunteer's, and one in the Citizen Army. They were wishing each other well and shaking hands. I heard one of the men say, "It's a great day for Ireland," as they moved off.

Old Mr McGuire was standing in his doorway. I asked, "What's happening Mr Mack?"

He said, "The army lads are reporting to their battalions. There's going to be fighting. They're taking over the Post Office."

"What post office I asked?"

"The G.P.O." he said, "It's a rebellion!"

"Who are they going to fight?" I asked.

"The English, of course," he answered, "They are setting up barricades in Church Street. And there's other fellas down on the Quays. You better go tell yer Ma."

I ran to the house Dinah and Ma were just cleaning up. I rushed in, Ma said, "For God's sake where are you running to?"

"Hey Ma, there's going to be fighting," I said.

"What are you talking about?" Ma said. I told her what Mr McGuire told me.

"Christy, go outside and see what's going on," Ma said.

Me and Christy went out. People were gathering in the street all talking about the situation.

"Come on" Christy said, "we'll run up to Church St and see what's happening." Off we went. When we got to Church Street, which is only a short distance from our house, there were soldiers from the Irish Volunteers overturning carts and piling furniture and barrels to block the road at North King Street. Soldiers had gone into the pub on the corner and were blocking the windows with mattresses. There were rifles sticking out the windows on the upper floors. One of the Men in a Green Uniform saw us and warned us to go home. "What's happening?" asked Christy.

The soldier answered, "We are going to fight for Irish Freedom."

"Is this like a war?" I asked.

"Yes," he said, "this is our war. Now get yerselves home. It will be dangerous around here in a little while."

"What will we do, Christy?" I said. "Let's go," said Christy. As we left, we could see the Irish soldiers building the barricade, some of them we not much older than us. When we got back to our street a lot of the neighbours were out on the street. The women had their Black shawls around them, and they looked worried.

Ma saw us and called us. "You are not to leave the street, stay where I can see you." The rumours were flying. The GPO was occupied, and The Four Courts had soldiers on the upper floors. Then we heard crowds of had gathered in O'Connell St They were watching as Volunteers occupied buildings all along the street. We were told that people were looting shops, there were no police around to stop them. No one knew for sure what was happening. We saw people coming down Mary St from O'Connell St loaded down with all kinds of clothes and household stuff, going on about it being for free.

After while we heard the sound of gunfire around the Four Courts area. We found out later it was along the Quays near Guinness's. A little while later we heard what we thought was gun fire coming from Henry Street. Fighting had erupted at the Castle and Irish volunteers had taken over the City Hall next door, The first casualty had happened here a policeman had been killed. Later we heard that there had been some English Lancers on horseback, and they were fired on by the Irish. They had actually charged up O'Connell St from Parnell St Some Soldiers had been wounded and several horses killed. Then it went quiet, we just had to wait and see what happened. An uneasy calm settled over the area.

Because it was a bank holiday, things had been quiet in the city, and the British army were slow to respond. We heard the whole country was supposed to be involved but there had been confusion as some of our leaders had not gotten orders to cancel all parades for that day. So, these soldiers were on their own. Also, we were told there were soldiers in Stephens Green and Boland's Mill and

Jacobs biscuit factory. So, all over the city there were areas blocked off. These sites were close to the main British Army Barracks so the British Army would have to get past these sites to get to the GPO, which we now knew was the main place for the Irish Army as we were now calling them.

The leader was Padraig Pearse he was the Commander of the Volunteers and James Connolly the Citizen Army. They had declared an Irish Republic and copies of the Proclamation were posted on some of the buildings with that message. As the day wore on, we heard a lot of shooting from along the Quays and around the Four Courts. Apparently, troops from The Royal Barracks had started to move along the Quays towards the GPO. All over the city there was shooting, it seemed far away. Ma made us say the rosary before we went to bed and Uncle Jerry came over to make sure we were all right. Uncle Jerry was saying, "If I was a younger man I'd be out there with the Boyos."

It was going to be hard to get to sleep. We lay in bed unable to sleep, and a little afraid I said, "Eh Christy, what's going to happen, will they be shooting at us?"

"No, but we are very close to where fighting is."

"If you were old enough, would you be with our lads I asked?"

"Of course, I would, we all would. It's our country, not theirs. We will have to be careful if we do go outside," Christy said.

"Ma won't let us out" I said. That night I dreamt of the Red Branch Knight's and Cú Chulainn.

The next morning, we woke as dawn was broke. There was no school because we were still on Easter holidays. As we sat around the table eating, we heard shooting. It was a machine gun firing up around North King Street. Then we could hear rifle fire from Church Street; it was very loud as we are close by. I heard Ma say, "God help those poor lads; it will be terrible. Now listen here you two, no going out till we know what's going on. I don't want any accidents." Pretty soon we could hear the machine guns firing quite a bit. Mr McGuire came in and told us that more soldiers were coming from Kings Bridge Railway Station and there was fighting in Parliament Street at the City Hall beside Dublin Castle, and around the Four Courts which is at the end of Church Street. He said it was snipers from the Irish Army shooting at them.

The Irish soldiers had also taken over a building on the south side of the Liffey near Guinness's. It was called the Mendicity Institute, it was a charity building that fed the poor people. There was a lot of shooting from there on the

English soldiers trying to move along the Quays. We were right in the middle of all this fighting. Inside the houses some people were panicking as the noise was getting closer. People told us the fighting had started along North King Street, we could hear the crack of the rifles.

Christy and I were going mad, we wanted to see for ourselves. Ma had to go over to Mrs Quinn who wasn't well to make sure she was ok. Me and Christy sneaked out the back and got over the wall into Abbey Street. It seemed quiet there, so we went over to Capel St to see what we could see. There were big English Army lorries unloading soldiers and they were heading to North King Street. We watched as they unloaded guns and ammunition and headed up towards Bolton St We were in a doorway looking on, when a British soldier saw us and shouted at us. "Get the fuck home ye little Fenian bastards."

We ran. No sooner were we in the door, "Where were you two?" Ma roared as she gave us a clip on the head, she was terrified that something might have happened us outside. It wasn't long before we heard the *rat-tat-tat* of machine gun fire on North King Street. Lucky, we had made it home. "Are you two listening! Do you hear that? You could get killed outside. This is serious, not the Pictures." We were really frightened now.

By nightfall there was a lot of smoke, and we could see the flames rising high over O'Connell Street. Firing was intense around Church St, and we heard some of the houses had been shot at, and there had been some of the ordinary people killed. Now we understood the danger. We all huddled together in our front room even Uncle Jerry who was with us looked worried. The night felt endless, it was impossible to sleep, we just dozed off sitting in the chairs. By the next morning there were all kinds of stories, we didn't know what to believe. The shooting continued and we were told O'Connell Street was wrecked and fires had broken out.

There was a battle being fought around the Grand Canal on the south side at Mount Street Bridge and there were a lot of English soldiers killed and injured. Troops had landed at Dun Laoghaire and were trying to get to Trinity College. They had to cross Mount Street Bridge and the Irish had set up snipers in some of the houses to guard the bridge. There was a big battle going on there. The sky was now black with smoke and the noise of gunfire, it was terrifying. We heard a commotion outside. There was someone banging on our neighbour's door.

Ma looked out, there were two Irish soldiers, one was wounded and needed attention, he was only a young lad. "Missus can you help me," one of the men said, "my pal is hurt. I was trying to get him to Jervis St hospital."

"Bring him in," Ma said, "maybe we can help." Ma brought him in, and they laid him on the bed. He was bleeding from a wound in his leg, there seemed to be a lot of blood. Ma and Dinah cut the leg of his trousers. The bullet had gone right through his leg. Ma washed it and she had bandages, so she bandaged it up and got the bleeding stopped. "You will have to get him to the hospital to get it checked, it could be infected."

"Hey mister, you will have to be careful, there was English soldiers in Capel Street."

"Christy!" Ma said.

"Can I look to see if its ok for them to go?" Christy said, "I'll sneak over the back wall. They won't see me and I'm only a kid."

"Mother of God," said Ma "You be careful."

"Can I go?" I asked. "No, you can't. Stay here it's too dangerous." Christy skipped out the back door and over the wall into Little Strand St We waited; it wasn't too long before he returned. "It's OK, the soldiers are up at the other end at North King St."

"Thanks son, that was very brave, I will get him to the hospital right away while the coast is clear. Thanks Missus." the soldier said.

"God Bless you, lads," said Mam. We watched them go, the injured one being helped by his friend. One of the men on the street saw them and offered to help. Between them they half carried him towards the hospital.

"Hey ma, that was very good of you to help," I said.

"If it was one of you, I would hope some other mother would do the same," she said.

By Thursday, the city was in chaos. The fighting in North King Street was brutal. One of the neighbours told us the British were breaking through the walls in the houses to get to where the Rebels were. They were shooting and killing ordinary men, women and even some children as they advanced. One woman's baby was killed in the pram by a stray bullet on Church Street. There had been shooting all around Stephen's Green and over by the Workhouse in Patrick Street.

It wasn't safe anywhere on the streets. The city centre was being destroyed. We heard an almighty bang and an explosion. The English were firing a cannon in O'Connell St They even brought a gun boat up the Liffey and shelled Liberty Hall and other parts of the city. Still the fighting continued through the day and night. That night as we tried to sleep there was a red hue in the sky as our city blazed. It looked like hell. The Rebels as they were now being called were losing ground as the British brought soldiers from all over to fight. By Friday we heard the G.P.O. had been abandoned and the leaders were now in Moore St On Saturday morning the fighting stopped. People said the Irish army had surrendered.

The Irish leaders decided to surrender in order to save civilian lives who were paying a high price due to the behaviour of the British Forces. Who would believe they would shell our city?

Chapter 3
Aftermath of Rising

As young boys it was hard to understand at first. We wanted the Irish to win but it wasn't a football match. People were dead and wounded. Our city was destroyed, there were English soldiers everywhere and they had the rifles with bayonets, and they were looking like they were ready to kill us. At first, we were frightened, then came resentment. This is our city, our country, why should we feel threatened in our home? People were stunned, there was mixed reaction to the rising. As I said before there were quite a lot of Irishmen fighting against the Germans in France, so the families depended on their pay to survive. So, the Rebels were not very popular. Then there's people like us who supported them and wanted our own country.

We watched as the Rebels were rounded up in and around Church St, some surrendered, and others just walked away, especially the younger ones who could blend into the crowds. The men looked exhausted their faces blackened by the smoke from the fires covered in dust, some with wounds yet to be treated. But as they stood together you could see the proud look in their eyes and feel the spirit emanating from them. Then they were marched away under guard. As we went into our house a feeling of sadness came over the place. Dinah was making our tea. I asked, "What will happen to the soldiers now, Ma?"

"I don't know, they will probably go to prison," she said.

"God Bless them, they will need our prayers anyway," Dinah said.

Ma said, "Now you two boys will have to be very careful especially when the soldiers are in the street. They may be very angry and take it out on anyone they can."

The next few days were very tense. Marshall law had been declared and there was a curfew. We had to be in by 6 o'clock and could not leave the house till 6 o'clock in the morning. On the Saturday there was no football, so we walked up to O'Connell St to see the damage. As we walked up Mary St to Henry St, we could not believe our eyes. There were still smouldering buildings and the G.P.O. was just a shell of a building. The whole street was demolished. There were still dead horses lying in the street. The smell of the burning buildings and the dead horses is something I would never forget. It would take years to repair. You could feel yourself getting angry, you would love to be able to bash the English for what they did this to us.

The Irish prisoners were kept in the grounds of the Rotunda Hospital, which was surrounded by English soldiers, they were to be taken to different English prisons in the city. The leaders were put in Richmond Barracks. People were wondering what would happen to the soldiers. Within a short time, it was established that the leaders would be tried for treason.

Lord French, the commander of the British Army, considered all the Irish Army not to be soldiers but traitors. He appointed Sir John Maxwell as commander of British Forces in Ireland. He immediately had Martial Law declared and left England to take up his new post as Commander of British Forces in Ireland. The British began rounding up any Volunteers they could lay their hands on. Many went on the run to avoid capture.

Thousands were arrested, even though only about 1200 men participated in the Rising. Most of the captured soldiers were shipped off to prisons in England, and a concentration camp in Frongoch in Wales. The Leaders were to be tried by court martial in a military court. Some of the so-called leaders were not the organisers at all, they were just ordinary soldiers. Padraig Pearse's brother Willie was one, Con Colbert was another and several others.

The seven men who signed the Proclamation were Pearse, Connolly, Clarke, Joe Plunkett, Sean Mc Diarmada, Eamonn Ceannt and Thomas McDonagh. Anyone who had been in charge of the battle sites were brought to Kilmainham. The country waited anxiously to see what would happen. We did not have long to wait.

The new General, when he arrived in Ireland to take command of the British Army, was Gen John Maxwell and he enforced martial law to the hilt. There were troops everywhere, and they were searching for Rebels. The R.I.C were helping them. It was said James Connolly had been badly wounded and taken to Dublin Castle where a hospital had been set up for wounded British soldiers. The Men in Boland's Mill and Jacob's had surrendered. There had also been fighting in Enniscorthy and Ashburn. But now it was all over. The majority of the Rebels had surrendered, somewhere in the region of 1200, another 1500 were rounded up and were shipped off to jails in England and Wales. Although the fighting had lasted only 5 days, it felt like months.

The British Generals wasted no time and by the next week started trying by court martial the main leaders of The Rising. The rising had started on the 24th of April and now it was only the 2nd of May. Padraig Pearse, Thomas Clarke, who was an old Fenian who had endured prison and torture by the British in the past, and Thomas McDonagh were convicted of treason and sentenced to death.

The following morning, they were taken out and shot at 3.00 am on the 3rd of May in the yard at Kilmainham. People were shocked. We couldn't believe the inhumanity of the British. These men were fighting for their own country and were soldiers not murderers. Next, we heard another four were shot on the 4th of May. On the 5th of May Sean McBride was executed with Willie Pearse, brother of Padraig, who was only a boy and Joseph Plunkett who was a poet. Joseph Plunkett had married his fiancé Grace Gifford in Kilmainham Gaol only hours before he was executed.

Michael O'Hanrahan and Edward Daly were next, these were not leaders but ordinary soldiers. It was disgraceful and public opinion started to turn against the British. A short time later, on the 8th of May, three more were executed. Sean Heuston, Con Colbert, these were only very young men and Michael Mallin a very famous piper; the people could not believe what was happening. There were protests from all over the world at the treatment of these men, still the British continued.

These men were soldiers not criminals, Thomas Kent was executed in Cork on May 9th. Last of all James Connolly was taken out of Dublin Castle hospital on a stretcher on the 12th of May where he had been imprisoned and treated for his wounds. He couldn't walk because of his wounds so they put him in a chair and shot him. There were another 98 men sentenced to death still in prison. But world opinion was strongly against any more executions, even the ordinary people of England were horrified by the actions of their government. These men were sent to jails in Ireland and England. All these so-called Rebels were convicted by a military court without the benefit of a proper defence. As far as we were concerned it was tantamount to Murder!

The country was reeling, people could not believe the savagery of the British Government. People who had jeered at the Rebels at the start were now praising the courage and dignity they had shown. There were more civilian casualties than military. North King Street saw the worst of the fighting in which civilians had been ruthlessly killed by soldiers burrowing through the walls of their houses to attack the rebel strong points. All across the city there were incidents of men, women and even children being murdered and killed or wounded whether on purpose or by accident, we will never know. These people were never mentioned by the British. In this environment it is understandable the effect it had on us. We would start growing up with a bitter taste for anything British and a desire to be free in our own country. And so, the Seed of Freedom was sown.

Chapter 4
Interim Period

We went back to school a few weeks later. All the talk among the boys was about the War and how when they got the chance they would join up in the Irish Army. The World War in France was still happening, and we read that at the Battle of the Somme the Irish Brigade had fought valiantly and Irishmen from both North and South had died in their thousands. What a waste; the country was sick of war.

It wasn't long to the end of the school year and I would finish at Strand St school and move to O'Connell's School. The school was run by the Christian Brothers who were renowned as great teachers. They also tended to be very patriotic towards a free Ireland. Needless to say, all these influences would eventually lead to my future as a soldier in the Irish Republican Army.

By 1917, a patriotic surge seemed to be taking over the country, a revival of Irish culture and music was flourishing. I was affected by this and I joined Na Fianna, an Irish boy scout's organisation founded by Countess Markievicz who was part of the Citizen Army and had taken part in the Rising. She was second in command of the Citizen Army in Stephens Green. She would have been executed if she had been a man. These were not just ordinary "Boy Scouts" but a training ground for future freedom fighters. We learned about map reading, camouflage and field drills. It also encouraged us to learn about our country, our heritage and our history.

Christy and I were still playing football and living as normal a life as was possible. Football was our only outlet away from the tragedy that had been the Rising. The year passed by without any more fighting. But the British Army now, along with the RIC, were regarded as our enemies. The British were now an Army of occupation. There were numerous raids and roadblocks around the city especially in the working-class districts as that is where most of the supporters of a free Ireland were to be found.

Then we entered 1918, as a fourteen-year-old I was at a crossroads in my life I had to decide what to do. I decided on a trade. Not having a father and seeing my mother working so hard I decided I would become an apprentice plasterer. As my mother's family had been in the trade, I could apply to be an apprentice plasterer. Being from a working-class family higher education wasn't really an option. So, at almost 15 I began work for Creedons, a firm noted for their work on all the finest buildings throughout the country. My brother Christy had also left school and was working as a clerk in one of the local offices. Molly was now full time in the market with Mam.

Times were so uncertain it was difficult to know the best thing to do. Mam thought about sending Christy to America where she had cousins in order to keep him safe. So, life in general just carried on. We learned to live with the situation as it was.

Then in November the World War finally ended. For us it wasn't really a time of celebration, we knew a lot of men would be returning home to their families, but then what. There was not a lot of work, especially for unskilled and under educated men. Dublin had some of the worst slums in Europe and parts of our city had been destroyed by the very people our lads had been fighting for. So, in these circumstances there was an uneasy feeling.

When 1919 dawned, we got new hope as the prisoners That had taken part in the rising who had been released were now organised as Sinn Fein a new political party of Irish men and women .These men and women were dedicated to "The Republic" and had honed their political skills toward that end. There were to be elections held for a new government. The old guard or Home Rule Party were not as popular as they had been before the war ended. People had at last realised that England held only contempt for the Irish people, their only reason for being here was for financial gain. The new party that would represent all the Irish People. Eamonn De Valera and several of the former prisoners would now run for office.

People got a sense of hope maybe we could finally have our own government in Ireland. The Sinn Fein party put up men in every county for election, and the people were with them. Some of the candidates were former prisoners. De Valera had been in command at Boland's Mill was the best known. By the time the election occurred several of these men became household names. Michael Collins among them.

The election took place, and the Sinn Fein party won an overwhelming majority. Only in the North did the Unionist party hold their own. These men were not going to take their seats in a British Parliament but were forming Dáil Eireann, our own Irish Government. They had a meeting in the Mansion House in Dawson St to establish the Dáil. There were crowds outside. Christy, Molly and me went up to watch the spectacle. It was like a holiday, everyone in great spirits watching the dignitaries arrive. We would give a big cheer when we saw someone we knew.

The candidates got a huge ovation as they went in. The atmosphere was terrific, people seemed happy. As we walked home, we passed through O'Connell St There still were areas that were just rubble. The GPO was a shell, just the front standing blackened by fire and burnt out. It was a sobering experience. Half of one of the most beautiful streets in Europe lay in ruins.

The British Government were shocked, at the election results, and as usual overreacted. They ordered the arrest of all the members of the Dáil. The Dáil members immediately went underground. Some were arrested and put into Kilmainham, some were taken to jail in England. The British Army and the RIC began a series of raids all over the country looking for Dáil members. In the meantime, the IRB began re-organising to combat the British efforts. Cathal Brugha had been made Chief of Staff. He organised "flying columns," consisting of volunteers who would attack throughout the country and then melt back into the population. Michael Collins, Minister of Finance and Intelligence, his ideas were quite different from the leaders of 1916. No more would we stand against superior forces to be slaughtered.

We would fight and pick our battles and terrorise the British making it impossible for Britain to govern us. Irish men again began to join the Volunteers to fight for freedom. Christy had joined the Volunteers; he joined the 2nd battalion Dublin Brigade. Part of his first assignment with the battalion had been making sure nobody interfered with the election. I was envious of him. He was learning about weapons and how we would fight against the British. Mam was terrified Christy would be arrested, all over the city British patrols stopped and searched civilians looking for IRA men. Christy given name was Charles, after his father, so if stopped he would say Charles and his name wouldn't appear on any list.

Chapter 5
Volunteers

So, by my 15th birthday, I had begun working and was enjoying it. I was out on a job one day helping to do some repairs to the ceiling of a church near the city centre, the cornices had been damaged due to the shelling during the Rising. I was working with one of the older men learning how to fix and fit pieces of plaster casts in place. We were high up in the roof as slates had blown off and the weather had damaged the ceiling. While we were working the door of the church burst open and a young man came running in. He ran down the aisle and disappeared behind the altar.

A couple of minutes went by and again the door was flung open and in came a group of soldiers with their rifles, shouting and swearing. The sergeant in charge looked up and saw us. He yelled, "Did you see a man run in here?"

Old Billy answered, "How could we see anyone from up here, we can hardly see you."

"Bollocks!" said the sergeant, "search the place."

With that the priest came out into the church. "What's going on here," he said, "have you no respect this is a house of God."

One of the soldiers put a revolver up to the priest's face. "We have no respect for you papist bastards, or your murdering IRA friends," the soldier said.

The sergeant shouted, "McFadden check out the front of the church see if you can see anyone." The soldier reluctantly lowered the gun and started searching around the altar and sacristy. We held our breath you could feel the tension the slightest thing would have caused mayhem. After a while they stopped searching and were getting ready to leave. The priest was still in the aisle standing, McFadden walked by whipped the revolver around and fired 3 shots blowing out one of the stained-glass windows. The noise was terrible. I thought he shot the priest.

"Oh," he said, "I thought I saw a Tighe standing there." They all left laughing. The priest looked up at us and shrugged "Dreadful people," he said and went back into the sacristy.

"We were shocked," Billy said, "I have to sit down, them fuckers were nearly the death of me."

I couldn't believe Billy was cursing, especially in the church. About half an hour later two priests came out of the sacristy. The one who had been confronted and a younger one with his hood up over his head. We heard him say, "Thanks father that was close. I'll see what we can do about the glass," and he left.

We were a little jittery getting back to work. I couldn't wait to get home and tell Christy about the incident. "I know all about it," Christy said, "it was one of our lads."

"What do you mean?" I asked.

"There was a raid on a van carrying some explosive material and one of the sections in our battalion ambushed it. They got some dynamite and stuff. They had to get away quickly. Some DMP were not far away and heard the commotion. Our lads had to scarper and one of them ended up in White Friar St Church. The priest there is a friend of our commander. The rest got away ok as well. Lucky the priest was in. He hid our man under the Altar in a vault, then dressed him like a priest so he could escape."

"Lucky we were up in ceiling of the church on the scaffold otherwise who knows what might have happened," I said. "The soldiers scared the shite out of old Billy and me too. I thought that madman of a soldier was going to kill the priest."

Towards the summer of 1919 I had filled out quite a bit and had grown a few inches where I was taller and heavier than Christy. I had jet black hair and had shadow around my chin which made me look much older than 15. I had made friends with a couple of lads who were going to join the volunteers. Michael Moran asked me if I would go with them to join. I decided it was the right thing to do, I knew lots of lads of my age and younger had fought in the 1916 Rising.

We went along to Parnell Square where we knew the place was to join up. When we got there were a couple of men outside watching. As we approached one of them came to us and asked, "What are you doing?"

"We want to join the Volunteers," we said. He looked us up and down, "Who told you to come over here?"

"A friend," I said.

"Who's this friend?" He asked.

"We can't say he might get into trouble," I said.

"But my brother is a volunteer, Christy Robinson, do you know him?" I asked.

He looked at me and said, "What's his nickname?"

I said, "Christy Boy."

"Ok," he said, "I'll get Frank to take you in." The other man called us over come on this way. We walked up the street and around the back of the buildings. There was another man on watch at the back. We climbed the stairs at the back to the top floor and went into a large room. There were three men inside on at a desk, the other two were chatting in the corner.

"What have we got here?," one of the men in the corner said.

Frank, who was with us, said, "These lad's want to join up." The man who had spoken came over and asked our names.

"I am Jeremiah Robinson," I said.

"I am Michael Moran," my friend said. "My name is Paddy Daly. Well now, why do you want to volunteer?" The man asked.

"We want to live in a free country," I said, "What do you know about freedom?"

"I know I don't like being pushed around by the British," I answered.

"Very well. You do realise that this is serious business, once you join there is no going back. Do you have any idea what we are doing?" He asked.

"Yes," I said, "I am already in the Fianna."

"You should have asked your leader in the Fianna about coming over here. We wouldn't have had to interrogate you as much. So, what we have to do is you have to take the Oath of Allegiance to the Irish Republic and be sworn in. Once you do that you will have joined up in the Volunteers as a rank and filer. Of course, you are both 17, the right age?"

"Yes," we both answered quickly. "I just have to be sure you both understand what is required of you." And so, without further ado we were sworn into the Irish Volunteers. I felt great pride as I mouthed the words that made me a member. To defend the Irish Republic!

"Now as new members you know you do not discuss what goes on here with anybody outside the organisation. And any kind of association with Crown Forces would be treason. Do you understand?"

"Yes," we answered. "From now on it is 'Yes Sir' to any Officer who addresses you."

"Yes Sir," we answered with enthusiasm. "You will be required to attend training on some nights and weekends. I assume you are both working. Depending on your skills you will be assigned to a battalion, where needed. Come back here on Saturday at 13.00 hours and we will get you organised," said Daly. As we left, we were again warned about talking about our involvement with the Volunteers. Walking home there was a different feeling inside me; it's hard to explain but it felt like I had transformed into a man in a very short time. I was bursting to tell Christy I had joined up. So just after tea him and I went out for a walk.

"Ok," said Christy "what is this all about? You have been like a hen on a hot griddle all evening."

"I joined up," I said.

"I thought as much," said Christy. "Who swore you in?" He asked.

"Paddy Daly," I said.

"The commandant himself," said Christy, "he's a good man." I told him I had to report on Saturday for training. "That's good, be careful going and coming from the HQ. Make sure no one knows what you are up to. Now mam will have twice as much to worry about."

"Yeah, I'm not looking forward to telling her. Still, I am sure she will understand that we just can't ignore the way things are going. I will tell her as soon as we get home so there is no trouble."

When we got home Mam and Dinah were in the kitchen having a cup of tea. As we walked in women's intuition kicked in, Ma knew there was something up. "OK you two, what's going on."

As I looked at Ma, I could tell she was expecting bad news. "I joined up in the Volunteers," I said. The blood seemed to drain from Ma's face, and she looked at me saying "Sure you are only a boy!"

"I am big enough to know what I have to do; things are changing, and we have to be involved," I said.

"May God forgive us, what did I do to deserve this?" Mam said.

Christy walked over to Mam, putting his arm around her shoulder he said, "It'll be alright Mam. There are a lot of Mothers in Ireland today who know the sacrifice that has to be made." I walked over and stood beside them.

Dinah came over and said, "I am very proud of both of you. God Bless you. I better give you a cuppa so," she said. It broke the tension, and we had a little laugh.

Chapter 6
Growing to Manhood

Time seemed to fly for me between working, training for football and now my involvement in the Volunteers. The following Saturday I made my way up to Parnell Sq. as instructed. Again, there were men on lookout duty on the street. I was told to wait around the back, and I would be picked up. At the back of the building there were a group of men waiting. I was surprised to see a man I knew, Vinny Byrne, there. He was organising us into teams.

"How is it going Vinny?" I said.

"Ahh good, Sam," he replied "It's good to see you here. But from now on its Sergeant Byrne when you speak to me ok."

I had forgotten Vinny had been out in the fighting in 1916, he had only been 14 years old. He was now an instructor in the Volunteers. He had been dropped out a back window in Jacobs by a priest that was helping with the surrender. We were picked up in a bread van, there were eight of us. We all climbed into the back and headed out for the Dublin Mountains for weapons training. Needless to say, we were excited. After an hour we found ourselves deep in the mountains at an old farm. There was an old cottage with a fire going and some sheep in the field beside it. Down a lane way was a larger building which was a barn. It had been set up as a training area. We were again divided up into smaller groups. There were tables laid out with different guns. I was with my friend Mick Moran and we had an instructor with us.

"These are the weapons you will get acquainted with," he said, "This is a Lee Enfield rifle. I am sure you have seen lots of these around, this is the standard rifle for the British army. Mostly in the city we use smaller weapons as they are easier to hide. This a six shot Smith and Wesson revolver, 38 calibre, we have a few of these. And this is the most effective of all, a Mauser 9mm, automatic. It can be used like a pistol or a rifle and it is deadly. As I said the Mauser is the best for us and is only given to our best men. The Lee Enfield is also a great rifle but too hard to conceal. They are used mostly by the flying columns in the country. You can handle these; they are not loaded but no horseplay and never point a gun at anyone unless you are using it. You have to learn how to maintain and care for your weapons and be able to strip and assemble them in the dark. A weapon that jams or misfires can get you killed or captured. Ok gather round and we will get started."

And so, we got our first introduction to weapon training. Before we knew it was time to return home. They had tea and bread and cheese in the cottage, which was welcome, it felt good to be part of an organisation that looked after its people. It was almost dark by the time we reached the city. We were dropped off down by the Four Courts as they did not want to draw too much attention to Parnell Sq. As I walked home, I realised I was now a Soldier.

As with any conflict ordinary life goes on. Days were flying by, working, football and now military training took up all my time. As time went by my focus began to be more on military training. The football was less important as the War of Independence which was taking hold of the community. Raids and searches by the British became constant. They were looking for IRA members or arms because of the type of war, the IRA was waging 'Hit and run' tactics. The British were unable to contain it. The attacks by the IRA on the RIC constabulary caused a shortage of manpower, so the British began to recruit ex-army personnel from the First World War in an attempt to control the situation. These men that joined up became the notorious BLACK and TANs.

They were a paramilitary organisation with no proper training and no discipline. Named because of their mixed uniforms of dark green of the RIC and khaki of the regular Army. In time they became a law unto themselves.

One day after work I met Christy on O'Connell St as we walked home. When we came to Mary Street there was a checkpoint and people were being searched. We had to pass through as trying to go back would draw attention to ourselves. The checkpoint was manned by some RIC with a squad of Tans. The RIC were doing the searching while the Tans watched. There was an old man that the Tan sergeant was bullying. He was pushing the man with his swagger stick and shouting, telling him to get his fucking hands up. The poor man was terrified. You could see him shaking with fear as the soldiers laughed and taunted him.

Without thinking my temper got the better of me. I said, "Leave the old man alone."

The sergeant looked up at me "Who do you think you are Paddy?" He said.

I answered, my face as red as a beet, "My name is not Paddy."

"Oh," said the Sergeant "a smart one." With that he smacked me across the shoulder with his stick. It felt like my shoulder exploded, the pain was fierce. I went down on my knees. The sergeant raised the stick again to hit me, then there was a shout from an officer who was close by, he shouted, "What's going on here?"

"Just teaching a Paddy some manners" the sergeant replied.

The officer came over. "Who are you?" He asked me.

"Jerry Robinson," I replied. I was hardly able to talk with the pain. "What happened here?" He asked.

I said, "Yer man was giving the auld lad a hard time. I asked him to stop."

The old man was still shaking as the officer looked at him. "Where are you going?" He asked me.

"I was on my way to training at the Park," I said.

"What training?" The officer asked.

I said, "Football. I play for Parade Rovers."

"Where's your gear?" he asked.

"The Coach has it," I said, "I can't bring it to work."

"What kind of football?" he asked.

"Ordinary football," I said.

"Ok get on with you, no more nonsense," he said, "Carry on Sergeant." As I left, the Sergeant grinning said, "I'll remember you Paddy," swinging his stick.

As we walked away Christy was fuming. "Don't draw attention to yourself like that," he said, "you have to control your temper. You could have got us arrested or worse. Lucky that officer believed you."

"My shoulder is killing me," I said.

"Lucky it wasn't your head," Christy said. We didn't go straight home in case we were being watched we took a roundabout way home. Needless to say, my mother was shocked when we walked in, she knew right away there was something wrong.

When we told her, she gave me a piece of her mind. "For God's sake be more careful. Take your coat off till I have a look at you shoulder." My shoulder had turned black and blue with a big welt across it. It was a lesson well learned to control my emotions.

Chapter 7
The Emerging Soldier

Over the next few weeks my military training became a priority. We had learned about weapons and had been drilling turning us into real soldiers. On Saturday we were going to be qualified on the various weapons with live ammunition. The day was overcast, and a little rain was falling as again we loaded into the bread van and headed for our training ground in Wicklow. The thought of real live ammo was exciting, a kind of coming of age for soldiers. When we arrived at the farm there were targets set up at various distances. First, we were again split into groups of four.

First of all, we had the Lee Enfield shooting at 100 yards. We had to shoot first lying in the prone position then kneeling and last standing. Our target was about 2 ft sq., at the distance we were at it looked small. We all felt a bit nervous. The instructors issued us with five rounds each. We lined up lying on the ground, I felt the stock of the rifle against my cheek and immediately felt comfortable. After going through the drill, we were told to fire in our own time, the object was to get as close to the centre as possible.

I remembered the instructors voice, "line up the sights, get a firm grip, take a big breath, let some out, then squeeze the trigger." I followed the instructions to the letter.

The crack of the rifle almost startled me as the site returned to the target, I worked the bolt to reload and settled on the same spot. Again, the rifle cracked, this time there was no sign of nerves and I continued till the exercise was over. The instructors collected the targets for examination. I was surprised to find I hit the target four out of five times very close together which was a good score. I was disappointed I didn't hit the bullseye, but the sergeant was pleased "that's good shooting the rifle may need adjustment." Through the day we continued, the smell of cordite became familiar as the shooting continued. After the rifle we had a break for tea and sandwiches.

"OK lads, we are going to shoot with pistols now, same groups." There were 3 different pistols, shooting at 25 yards we all got to try each one. By the end of the day we were all singled out according to how good we had been. I had scored the highest, I had qualified with all the different weapons.

Vinny Byrne came over to me, "How long have you been shooting?" He asked.

"Today was my first time with a real gun. I shot a pellet gun at the carnival a few times. I love shooting," I said.

"I guess you are a natural. We need people who can shoot straight," said Vinny.

"How do you think you would do if there were real people or someone shooting back?" He asked.

"I don't know. I hope I would do my best, I guess you have to do it to find out if you have the balls for it," I answered.

"OK," Vinny said, "I am sure we will find out." By the time we got back to the city it was starting to get dark and a drizzle of rain was falling. I got dropped off at the Four Courts along the Quays. Walking along a couple of lorries passed full of soldiers. They gave me a look as they passed, they were heading towards O'Connell St I paid no notice and kept walking; I was relieved when they kept going. I didn't need another brush with them. As I went into the house Ma and Dinah were in the kitchen making the tea.

"Where were you until this hour? It's nearly 8 o clock!" Ma said.

"You know them fellas are only waiting for an excuse to hassle you."

"Yeah, we got delayed a bit," I said. "What's for tea?" changing the subject I asked.

"I have a coddle," Dinah said.

"Good" I replied, "I'm starvin'. Is Christy home?"

"He's at your uncle Jerry's next door, he will be in soon for his tea," said Mam. The smell of the coddle was mouth-watering, after a day in the mountains it was just the ticket.

After tea Christy came in when we were on our own, "How did it go today?" He asked.

"Great," I said, "It was great fun."

"Yeah it's a buzz on the range, not so much when it's for real."

43

"What do you mean? Have you been on a job?" I asked.

"I'll tell you after," Christy said. When we were on our own, he told me. "A few weeks ago, we had a job, it all went a little hairy. The information was wrong and there were more soldiers than we expected. One of our lads panicked and fired of a couple of shots before we were ready. Next thing we knew the soldiers were shooting at us. We had to break off and run, but we managed to get away. We knew the back streets and they were afraid to follow us. But next day they raided the houses in the street, and they wrecked a couple of the houses. God help them they gave the people an awful time. They had nothing to do with us. So just be careful and keep everything to yourself. OK?"

The week went by quickly I was at work and was busy. When Saturday came around, I went back to HQ again I made sure I was not followed. The commandant was there and a few of the men. He called me over and spoke to me. "I have been looking at your performance and you have been assigned to E Coy. 1st. Batt. As of now you will report to Jim Slattery from now on. He is up the street. Charlie will take you over."

"Thank you, Sir. I won't let you down."

"Good, carry on," he said. Charlie walked me over and introduced me to Jim Slattery of my new unit.

"Hello Sam. Now this is a small unit which gets special jobs from the Big Fella. You will let us know where you are going to be, from time to time you may have to skip work ok. Some of the lads are working on a couple of assignments, just listen and learn they know what they are doing."

I went over and the lads welcomed me. Without being specific they were planning to hold up a couple of Post Offices. As well as getting money we also would disrupt the mail which caused havoc with the Government. I would be on guard at one end of the street while two others held up the clerks and grabbed what we needed. Another man would be at the other end of the street.

Watching for police or soldiers I would cover the getaway. Billy said, "This is a fairly routine operation, and we don't expect much opposition. But you never know so you have to be on your toes. Remember only RIC or soldiers are armed, Dublin police are not. So usually, a warning is enough for them. We will meet up on Monday morning here at 8.00am. See you then. By the way if you have a suit wear it. Soldiers tend to go after labourers rather than well-dressed fellas, plus you will blend in better. Dismissed!"

So, I headed home my mind racing I was now going into action for the first time. I don't know whether I was scared or excited.

Sunday morning was as usual Ma's breakfast after Mass, and I had a football game after dinner which helped to take my mind off Monday morning. I enjoyed the game, I managed to concentrate and played reasonably well. We ended up winning 3 to 1. Walking home from the park it got dark and started to rain. I hoped it was not a sign of things to come. Because the curfew had been lifted, we could go out in the evening till 10 o'clock. There was a ceili dance at the hall in Church Street. My pal Mikey asked me to go with him as he was expecting to see a girl he fancied. I wasn't crazy about going but thought it might be a bit of fun. "It's only for a couple of hours," Mickey said, "we'll have a laugh."

We walked over to Church St Hall. There was a decent crowd there and they all seemed to be enjoying themselves. The lads were all together on one side while the girls were on the other side. These dances were organised by Cumann na Mban, the female version of the Volunteers. Some of the women had been involved in the Rising in 1916. The women here were here to make sure we all behaved. They served tea and soft drinks; no alcohol was allowed. Mikey made a bee line for his girlfriend, and I took up a spot where I could see the dancers. I did not know how to dance.

I was enjoying the music; it was lively, and the place was bouncing to the dancer's steps. One of the women passing me said, "Are you holding up the wall, you should be dancing."

I turned beet red. A couple of the girls heard her and started giggling. I got even more embarrassed. One of the girls turned to me. "Would you like to give it a try?" She asked, "It's not that hard."

"Ok," I said. "When this set is over, I will show you OK" she said. When the set finished, she took my hand and led me onto the floor. "Now just follow what the men do and listen to the music that will give you the timing."

"This dance will be the Walls of Limerick," the band announced. As we got going, I tried to concentrate and after a while I got a little more confident and managed keep up without knocking anybody down. By the time the dance ended I was exhausted. I thought football was hard, this was tougher. Of course, wearing a suit and tie jumping around made it very hot. At the end, the girl asked, "So how was that?"

"Great," I said, "I enjoyed it."

"Well now you have no excuse, you won't be able to hold up the wall anymore." We got talking and found out her name was Annie and she had come down with a few of her friends from Dominick St I enjoyed talking to her and tried one more dance before it was time to leave. We all walked together down to Capel St where we parted company as they headed towards Bolton St I promised to go the next Saturday for more lessons.

By the time I got home I felt tired and thought I would sleep like a log, but my mind was racing thinking about the morning. It was going to be a fitful night.

The morning broke, cloudy with a threat of rain. I got dressed in my suit with a tie. Mam was already at the market. As I sat to have breakfast Dinah looked at me and said, "What are you all dressed up for are you not going to work?"

I was evasive with my answer. "I have something special on after work, I will put my overalls over my suit." I don't think she was convinced. While walking over to Parnell Sq. I was even more aware of people, looking for anything out of the ordinary as I made my way to HQ. Our unit was assembling there, seven men altogether, four with guns and another two men who were lookouts and one on a postman's bike. Jim Slattery issued the weapons I was given a Mauser pistol with a folding stock with two extra magazines. The others had Parabellum 9mm. We were leaving in twos by a roundabout way. Our target was a Post office on Dame St close to the Castle. There was a laneway four doors down from the post office that led to a backyard of the post office. Our lookouts were posted at each end of the street.

We had a system so we could warn each other of any danger. I set myself up at the corner of the lane. There were some bins in the lane which gave me some cover. I had the weapon under my overcoat within easy reach if I needed it. On the other side of the road our other man was stationed in the entrance to one of the buildings. It had big pillars and was a good place. This post office handled a lot of the mail for the Castle where British Intelligence was based. So, one of our tasks was to grab as much government mail as we could. There was a young lad dressed as a post man standing by with a bike that could carry the mail. Our lads entered the post office through the back entrance.

As I waited, I kept my eyes peeled. I was a bit nervous but was reassured by the feel of the gun under my coat. Time went by very slowly; our men were inside for only minutes.

As I watched I heard a commotion in the post office. One of our men came running out holding two bags, the other man came out with a drawn pistol covering the entrance. There was someone shouting inside trying to raise the alarm. The fella came charging out, as he did our man hit him on the head with the pistol, and down he went down unconscious. I in the meantime had drawn my weapon and was covering him ready for action without even thinking about it. The shouting hadn't been noticed. The boy on the bike showed up and both bags disappeared.

We hid our guns under our coats and started walking away. As we left two policemen came running towards us, with our weapons already concealed, we just continued to walk away. They gave us a look, we ignored them and turned down one of the small streets towards the quays. We just melted into the people and managed to slip away. I didn't realise until later my legs were like rubber, and I was shaking. There was a safe house in Abbey Street where we dumped our arms then we continued on to Parnell Sq. to give our after-action report.

When we got to our HQ our Commandant Jim Slattery was waiting. "Everything go OK?" He asked.

Pat Dunne answered, "Yes Sir. Most of the staff were cooperative, they were local people except for one. We had to clip one of the workers, he got too excited and wanted to raise the alarm! Otherwise, no problems."

"Did you manage to dump your arms?" Slattery asked.

"Yes, the contact was waiting for us."

"How did Sam do?" He asked.

Dunne answered, "He was Ok, no obvious nerves."

"Good, now head out one at a time and we will meet here tomorrow night at 19.30 hours. Good Job, some of the mail in the bag was helpful and our funds have increased considerably. Sam, I need a word with you," Slattery said.

"Yes Sir," I answered.

After the others had left, Slattery came over to me. "Have a seat," he said, "What did you think of today's action?"

I said, "It was pretty straight forward, we were well organised and other than the fella running out it went like clockwork."

"Yes," said Slattery, "when the jobs are planned properly, they normally go Ok, but you never can tell when it will all fall apart, and you have to be able to think on your feet. I have a feeling you would be able to handle a situation like that. We are forming a new unit called the Active Service Unit. It's the Boss's idea, I want to put your name forward. It will be made up of full-time soldiers, mostly single men, who will be required to be available on a 24-hour basis. It may also require you to be on the run and sometime stay at safe houses.

Do you think you would be able to do that? I want you to think about it and give me an answer tomorrow. There is no shame in thinking you could not do it, you, would still be part of the Battalion. If you join the ASU you will be paid as a full-time soldier. Off you go I'll see you tomorrow."

I walked around a bit so I wouldn't be home too early. My mother usually would be home about 2 o'clock. As I walked in my Ma said, "How come you didn't go to work today? Dinah told me you went out all dressed up."

I looked at my Ma and knew I couldn't lie to her. "I had a job on with the boys today," I answered.

Ma's face seemed to lose all its colour. "Sacred Heart of God, you mean the IRA?"

"Yes, Ma," I answered "I am part of the army now. We have to do things from time to time. You Know that."

"I didn't realise you would be needed so soon," Mam said, "I have hardly gotten used to Christy being involved. You are only a boy."

"I know it's hard Ma, but we have to do what we think is right. I'll be Ok, try not to worry."

"It's easier said than done," Ma said, "Please be careful, I lost your father I don't want to lose my sons. That would kill me altogether."

I felt sorry for Mam, she worked hard and had had a hard life so far with the loss of her husband so young and working in the market. She was made of strong stuff; I knew in my heart what I would do, I felt strongly about our cause I was confident I could do the job. I went into work the following day and found it hard to concentrate on the work, I had made my mind up and I was going to join the new unit if I was accepted.

At dinner that evening I don't think I even tasted the food I was preoccupied thinking about how I would tell my Mam, but I knew I had to be straight with her. As we were drinking our tea I said to Mam, "I have something to tell you Ma. I have been asked to join a new unit in the army, if selected it would make me a full-time soldier. I know how you feel but I want to join. I couldn't go ahead without telling you." Mam turned to Christy, "Did you know about this?"

"No Mam, I didn't," Christy said. "Will you be doing the same?" She asked.

"No Ma'am, I am with a different group; this is up to Sam," he said.

Ma looked stricken. "I suppose I will have to get used to the idea that I have sons who are soldiers. It won't be easy." With that she came over to me, put her hands on my shoulders and said, "God be with you. I will go over to the church and say a few prayers."

Me and Christy went outside, I was going to HQ. He just tagged along for a bit. "So," he said, "you will be with the Big Fella. I heard he was going to do something new."

"I have no idea, I have to be accepted first," I said.

"Don't worry, you will be ok, just keep your temper under control. Good luck," he said as he walked away.

Chapter 8
ASU

When I got to HQ there was an air of excitement about the place, there were two armed guards, one outside and one inside the door. I had to give my name to the one on the stairs and he checked to make sure who I was. "Go to the top floor," he said. I headed up; at the top there were two big rooms. Jim Slattery and Paddy Daly were looking over some papers. When Slattery saw me, he nodded and told me to wait he would see me shortly. I just stood and tried to look calm even though my mind was racing I wanted to know if I was going to be accepted.

After a few minutes Paddy Daly came over. "How is it going Sam?" He asked.

"Good Sir," I said. "You fellas did a good job the other day, we got some good info from the mail bags. You know why you are here," he said, "You have been recommended to the ASU our new full-time unit, I've been checking up on you and I like what I see, we will have to see if the boss thinks you are ok. Come with me."

We went across the landing and Commandant Daly knocked on the door. It was opened by an armed guard. As we walked in, there sitting behind a desk was 'The Boss,' Michael Collins, he was studying some papers. My mouth was dry as I looked at him. I stood to attention, he looked up.

"What have we here Paddy?" He asked.

"Sir, this volunteer, Sam Robinson," Paddy said, "he has been highly recommended for the ASU."

Collins looked me over, "Jesus wept, Paddy I am not running a kindergarten. How old is this child?"

Without thinking I blurted out, "I am old enough, don't you worry I will do the job." My face must have turned purple.

"Well now," said Collins, "at least you have spirit. What do you think Vinny, can we use this fella?" I hadn't realised Vinny Byrne had opened the door. He had been my instructor in charge of training.

Vinny was smiling, "Yeah I think we can make a soldier out of him." I didn't know where to look and was totally embarrassed by my outburst.

Collins looked up at me and laughed, "Well now that that's out of the way, you understand what may be required of you. We will not be fighting by the Marquis of Queensbury rules and sometimes we will have to do things that are very hard to stomach. Do you think you will be able to do that?" I thought for a moment before answering. "Yes, Sir, I see every day the cruelty of the British and the RIC. I don't think I will have a problem."

"At least you are not wrapping the green flag around yourself, we need to be able to make decisions and act accordingly. OK, Vinny will take you down to see your new boss, he will get you squared away." He stood up, he was taller and heavier than me with a shock of brown hair. He stuck his hand out and I took it feeling the strength in him.

"Welcome to ASU and good luck." I stood to attention and said, "Thank you sir I won't let you down." That meeting was to change my life as I knew it. I would now become a full-time soldier in the fight for Irish Freedom. Also meeting Michael Collins, I felt a new sense of belonging. There was an aura about Collins and knew I would follow him to the end.

When I got home that night Christy was waiting for me. "Let's take a walk for a few minutes." We went outside across to Ormond Quay and stood by the river. The evening was cool and felt like rain wasn't too far away. "So how did it go?" Christy asked.

"Well, I'm in," I said, "I report tomorrow for more training and get to know the lads."

"That's great but be careful."

"I met Mick Collins," I said.

"Did you now! The big man himself," said Christy. "He said I was only a boy and of course I couldn't keep my mouth shut. I said I was old enough and well able to do the job."

"You're mad!" said Christy "one of these days you're going to open your mouth when you should keep it closed."

"Collins said I had spirit and he was ok after that. He is quite the man," I said, "he has a presence about him I can't explain but he sure made an impression on me."

As we headed home a couple of army lorries passed by us with troops heading towards the Royal Barracks. It brought back reality watching as they passed knowing that sooner or later, I would be taking these fellas on. I took a little shiver, and we went home. The following morning, I went into work as usual, I explained to my boss that I would not be coming back he said, "If you change your mind let me know."

I had orders to report to Abbey Street where we had dumped our arms after the post office job. It was a cabinet maker's shop which was a front. It was also where the ASU worked out of, with members of the 'Squad' which were Michael Collins elite gunmen who worked directly for him. From time-to-time ASU men were drafted in to help in larger operations. Abbey St was a short walk from where we lived in East Arran St When I arrived, I was surprised to see lads working making pieces of furniture it looked like a proper business. Going in I was aware of being watched, the foreman in his shop coat saw me and came over. "Good morning what can I help you with?" He said looking hard at me.

I had to think how to answer. "I was told to come over to see if you needed any help."

"I see, well come with me," he said. We went to the back of the building and through a heavy door. There was a big area with some benches and a couple of lads were working there. The foreman turned to me and said, "You must be one of the new men, I wasn't expecting you so early. My name is Joe Leonard, I am in charge at the moment. There will be two more men down soon and we will get you all sorted. In the meantime, these lads are making up some grenades, you can watch and learn. I watched as the lads filled small tins with explosive and nails with small wicks sticking out."

I asked, "How good are these?"

The older of the two looked at me. "They will do the job if you can get in close enough. You have to light the wick; it will burn for five seconds then hopefully explode. It should give you time enough to get out of the way. It's all we have at the moment. These are to attack lorries; you throw it in the back or underneath the cab. I have been told it scares the shite out of the soldiers when they see the smoke from the wick. Just one of the tricks we use!"

52

While I was watching, Joe Leonard came over and introduced me to Jim Sullivan, "Go with Jim and he will get you used to our patrol area around our base." Jim was a big lad like me. We were both dressed in suits. We went to the arms dump at the back and were given a revolver each. The guns were .38 colts and fitted in our suit pockets easily.

"Ok," Jim said, "first things first, check your weapon and make sure the safety is on you don't want to shoot yer foot off." I was able to secure my gun in my inside pocket where I could get it quickly.

Then we set out. "Ok," said Jim "Our job is to patrol around the shop and keep our eyes open for police or Tans. Next time you will be on your own, our street is not a usual route the Tans take so any sign of them in this area is dangerous." We headed down to Capel St The area was a busy shopping place and there were lots of people out and about. "Just keep your eyes open and anything that looks out of place take a second look, to be sure. Have you been out before?" Jim asked.

"I was on a couple of jobs but no real action yet."

"Well, that's the way we want to keep it today," said Jim. Capel St is a route to the Castle so you will see military traffic on the bridge. Just watch they don't head up towards our place.

"What do we do if they come this way?"

"Get back as fast as you can and warn the lads. They can have the back closed down in minutes. If things look serious, we might have to create a diversion. One time we started a fight in the street with a couple of men to draw the police away, anything that works. If we had to, we would take a couple of shots and make a getaway. That's the last option."

So, we continued to patrol our streets looking for danger that may occur at any moment. Walking those streets, I felt apprehensive knowing I was responsible for the safety of my fellow soldiers. That was my start as a full-time soldier. There was never a routine as such, as we were on the defensive most of the time, we had to pick our battles knowing we had a good chance of success. The new year of 1920 had brought an increasing ferocity to the battle. Reprisals by the crown forces had the general public on our side. We needed them on our side as they often shielded us when we were in dire need. I'll give you an instance. Our unit were out to stage an attack on the military. We were on Aungier Street, a route the Military used to get to Portobello Barracks. This area was known to the British as 'The Dardanelles' after a WW1 battlefield.

We were spread out with two men armed with grenades. They were going to do the throwing at the lorry while the rest of us covered them. We were all armed with revolvers and one automatic. We took up our positions at the intersection where five streets came together, the main street running north on his right. The target would pass his position first and he would give covering fire to the first bomber. Two others to my right, one across the road firing from vacant building giving him an elevated view of the target. The second bomber would aim for the cab.

With the Bombers between us one on each side of the road. Two men with a hand cart with bags of coal would push the cart into the path of the lorry to slow it down. We waited my mouth felt dry my hand on the gun in my pocket. This was the real thing, how was I going to act when I needed to. People were just going about their business it was just another day in Dublin. As I watched all our men were ready and in position. Then we could hear the sound of engines heading our way.

There was a car coming down from Camden Street and the lorry approaching in the opposite direction, the hand cart full of coal was being pushed up the lane behind where I was standing. The sound grew louder as the lorry changed gear on the hill. The lads pushed with all their might and got the cart out almost to the centre of the road, the lorry kept coming and was going to brush the cart aside. We could see the soldiers in the back, there was about 12 men in the back and 3 in the open cab.

Then we noticed there was a wire covering across the back which made it hard as the men with the grenades would have to attack from the rear. I thought our section leader was going to stand us down as he looked like he didn't like our chances. All of a sudden, our first man with the grenade rushed towards the back of the lorry before anyone could move, he lobbed it into the truck bed. There was smoke from the grenade which caused the soldiers to panic and start jumping out, as our man raced away the soldiers began to raise their rifles aiming at our man.

Without thinking I had my gun in my hand and fired into the soldiers at the rear of the truck, the rest of the section open up and bullets were flying in all directions. People started running for cover. Our man in the vacant house fired at the driver. The driver was hit, and the lorry slewed across the road facing us smashing the coal cart as it went. Now stopped and the soldiers using it for cover, our first grenade did not explode our second grenade was thrown out under the lorry, it exploded sending smoke and debris all around us.

I had good cover and was able to avoid the shrapnel. Some people were screaming and there was a couple of soldiers lying on the ground with injuries caused by the bomb. The car coming down from the canal swerved across the road and went on the footpath and ran into a pole smashing a shop window. Then we heard another engine, it was a Crossley tender full of military coming up from the Castle. Our leader gave the signal to withdraw. Immediately we dispersed in different directions, I passed the now wrecked hand cart with the coal and darted down the Peter's Row towards Jacob's Biscuits factory.

It was lunch hour and several of the girls were outside getting some air. They had heard the commotion and were starting to run back inside they all wore aprons with big pockets. I was confused and a bit shocked. One of the women from Jacobs was looking at me terrified. She asked, "Are you alright?"

As I looked at her, I realised why she was frightened, I still had my revolver in my hand. Again, she asked, "Are you ok?" As she said it, she it she looked at the gun. "You better hide that," she said, "the police will be here any minute."

I hesitated and began to put the gun in my pocket. "Here," she said, "give it to me, I'll hide it for now. I know someone who'll get it back to you." With that she took the gun, put it in one of her big pockets and went inside into the factory. I turned away and began to walk down the street towards the city centre.

Luckily, I didn't get covered in debris, my clothing was still ok. No sooner had I reached Dame Street the police were just setting up check points looking for us. I only managed to get passed without being checked. Our orders were to go over to an old yard in Smithfield to dump our arms and report. By the time I got there I was back to my normal self. I had just had my baptism of fire and I at least I had scraped through. I was a bit embarrassed when asked for my weapon, explaining to my section commander that I gave it to a woman in Jacobs was difficult.

He said, "Good thinking, it will turn up ok." It did.

Chapter 9
Dark-Haired Girl

The next few weeks were quiet for us, again back on patrol around our Abbey St location. I was also tasked with carrying messages between our constantly moving HQ. On one of these occasions as I was making my delivery to Vaughn's Hotel I went up to the room and knocked on the door. The Chief himself opened the door to me. "How are you doing Boyo?" he asked. I was shocked to see him, and it took me a few seconds to reply. He laughed and said, "Lost our voice have we. It's Sam, isn't it?"

"Yes, Sir," I answered "I am fine."

"Good, I am glad, we need to keep sharp. Are you going back to Abbey Street?"

"Yes, Sir," I answered. "Ok. Take this message to Joe Leonard. Be careful so, the Castle boys have been very busy lately." As I left, I was astonished to know the 'Big Fella' as we called him remembered my name. On my way back I was extra careful, just making sure I wasn't followed.

I went home to my mother's house that evening. I hadn't been there for a few days. "You must have smelt the grub," Dinah said as I walked in.

"Where have you been?" Ma asked. "I had to move around a little just in case someone was watching."

"Are you Ok?" Ma said, "Where did you sleep?"

"We have a couple of places we can stay," I answered.

"Anyway," she said, "It's good to see you, sit down and get stuck in. We've a lovely bit of fish."

"I swear you must have smelled it from the street," Dinah said a big smile on her face now she had someone to look after.

"Is Christy home?" I asked. I hadn't seen him for about a week. "He was here last night, I am not sure if he'll be home for tea."

"Is Mollie about?" Dinah whispered, "she's supposed to be going over to the church but I've a feeling she is meeting a fella. She was all done up, not exactly dressed for church. Don't say anything to your Ma." It felt good to have a little bit of normality in my life. Being a soldier in an underground Army was stressful especially for a 16-year-old.

After tea I decided to get some air, outside I met Mikey McGuire. "Howaya Sam, haven't seen you around much lately?" He said.

"I've been busy ye know how it is," I answered. "I'm headin' over to the hall tonight do you want to come it should be good, there's a bird I'm chasin' going," said Mikey.

"Yeah, why not, it might be fun," I said.

We walked over to the hall. When we got to the hall it was in full swing good music and the crowd enjoying themselves. I parked myself at the wall as usual watching the proceedings, listening to the music. "There ye are now we haven't seen you for a while."

It was Annie, the girl that had me up dancing the last time. "I hope you haven't forgotten all I taught you," she said. I just laughed thinking about my last dance.

"We will get you up again tonight. There's nowhere to hide," Annie said with a smile. A couple of the lads came over for a chat.

Mikey came over, "Do you see your woman over there, the good lookin' one, I am going to ask her out," he said.

"Does she need glasses?" I asked with a smile. Mikey looked up at me then it clicked! He gave me a light punch on the arm. "Smart Arse," he said.

As he walked towards the girl Annie came over to me. "Come on now their starting a new set." She took me by the arm and led me to the floor. As soon as the music started, she was giving instruction. "Follow me do as I do."

After I got over my shyness, I began to enjoy myself. Time flies when you're having fun. When the set ended Annie brought me over to meet her friends. There was this lovely small dark-haired girl standing talking to another girl. "Now girls this is our new dancer, his name is Sam."

The girls laughed. "So nice to meet you," they said.

"I'm Kate," the dark-haired girl said, "and this is MaryAnne." As Annie walked over to some other group.

"Hello," I said not knowing what to say. Small talk was not my strong suit. I must have been blushing as Kate smiled at me. "Don't mind Annie, she knows everyone, she helps to organise the dances and gets all of us involved." Just then a new dance started, it was a waltz.

Kate looked at me and asked, "Do you know how to waltz?" I just shrugged my shoulders. "Ok," she said, "if you promise not to kick me, we can give it a go." As we started dancing, I lost myself in the moment. It was the first time I had ever held a girl in my arms, and it felt good. I even managed, with Kate counting, to finish without tripping up or standing on her toes. The night went very quickly before we knew it was time to go home.

We walked out of the hall and started home. Annie and the girls came out. "I'll walk with you if you like," I said, "You never know what can happen on the streets these days."

"That would be nice," said Kate.

"So, what do you do with yourself when you're not dancing?" Annie asked.

"I work in the building and play a bit of football," I answered. "That's grand, keeps you busy so."

"What do you do?" I asked.

"We all work in Jacobs making biscuits," Kate said.

"That's a good job," I said, "in out of the weather." They all laughed.

"What's weather got to do with biscuits," Annie said. "I couldn't think of anything else to say." So, we continued on till Dominick St.

"Ok, goodnight," I said. As I began to walk away, I got the courage to say to Kate. "Would you like to go out sometime?"

"That would be nice. I'm off next Saturday afternoon, I could meet you then," said Kate.

"Yes, ok," I said, "I'll see you at 3 o'clock outside the Church."

"That's great," I said and left walking home with a spring in my step. I realised I was smitten. Emotions were something I had never given much thought to other than, how I felt about my family and the cause were fighting for. Now I was realising I had other feelings and need.

Chapter 10
Things Heating Up

It was now September 1920 and myself and Christy were now deeply involved. I was at a safe house over in Smithfield staying with two of the other men from my Company. It was about 2 o'clock in the afternoon when Pat Brennan came in. "Howaya Pat," I said. When I looked at him, I knew there was something wrong.

"We have to get out of here now! There's been an ambush by H Coy. and it was a disaster. Did you not hear the shooting, it was only over at Church Street?" He said.

"No, we never heard anything, the factory next door is working so there was a lot of noise," I said. "Anyway, he said we have to clear out of here sharpish or else we'll be trapped here. You know the drill, good luck." I grabbed my stuff making sure my Parabellum was loaded. I put on a topcoat to cover the weapon and headed out. There was always more than one exit in the houses we stayed in, I headed out the back way. I cut through a yard that led down towards the Quays. I heard the sound of engines, a Crossley tender full of Tans came tearing around the corner heading towards North King St I ducked into a shop as they passed by.

They stopped about 200 yards up the street and started to block off the street. I ducked into a shop, it was a shoemaker shop, there was only the one man working on a last fixing a shoe. I looked out the window at the Tans setting up. The shopkeeper gave me a knowing look. "Maybe you should go out through the lane way at the back, it might not be so busy."

"Thanks," I said as he opened a door leading into a lane that led down towards the markets which were very busy, and I was able to blend in with the people. I was going to go into our house when Mr McGuire waved to me warning me not to go in. He nodded in the direction of Abbey Street as if I was to follow him which I did. We went around the corner to the lane way where the Old Abbey building was. There was a hallway we could step into.

"What's up?" I said, feeling concerned. "There was a lot of police activity around here yesterday they may be watching your house yesterday. The detective with them was nosing around he wasn't from around here. He could have had a tip, so I was nervous that he was watching for you or Christy. Just to be sure I didn't want you going in. I heard there was trouble in North King St."

"Good thinking," I said, "Thanks. I'll be careful." We both went away in different directions.

I headed down too Little Strand Street, my Ma's sister lived there. Aunt Mary answered the door. "Sam! Come in it's been a while since you were here," she said looking up and down the street.

"Yes," I replied "just passing, I thought I'd say hello."

"That's nice, come on in we'll have a cup of tea and have a chat," she said closing the hall door. She asked, "What in the name of God is going on? Your brother is upstairs, and he is shook!" she said.

"I'm not sure but there is a lot of Tan activity up around Church Street. I had to get out in a hurry," I replied. Christy came down the stairs, he slipped his revolver back into his pocket as he did. "Christy I was just about to go into our house when Mr Mac. told me not to. He said someone was watching!"

"I know," he said, "I got the nod not to go home." Christy had on his brown suit, so I knew he had been out on a job. Aunt Mary went into the scullery to get water for tea, we went up to the room at the top of the stairs. "What a fuck up," Christy said when we were out of earshot.

"What happened?" I asked.

"We were to hold up the army lorry picking up bread at Monk's Bakery on North King Street and take their weapons. We had it nailed when another Crossley tender full of Tans came along. One of the soldiers grabbed for his rifle and opened fire. We returned fire and a fight started, we started to retreat. A couple of the soldiers fell. One of our lads, our section leader Kevin Barry, was to cover us from the other side but his gun jammed. He hid under a lorry, we had to run for it."

"When the lorry began to move a woman screamed that there was a man underneath and the soldiers got him. One of our other lads was wounded, they managed to get him to the Richmond hospital before the Tans arrived. I was lucky to get away down Beresford Street before they cordoned it off."

"That's two of us that got lucky today," I said.

Things were getting worse in Ireland, in the country there had been many reprisals and atrocities committed by crown forces, tit-for-tat killings were commonplace. Michael Collins felt Castle Intelligence, the Cairo gang as they were called, were getting too close and was planning an operation to deal with that situation. In the meantime, we kept a low profile. We were trying to be as normal as possible without bringing any notice to ourselves.

I walked around the city as if I had someplace important to go, always dressed in a suit and tie. It was easier to get passed any police cordon that might pop up, I always had a letter from a solicitor's office on me that I was supposed to be delivering to a client. That's the cover I used a lot. Also, my name being Jeremiah helped as any list I might have been on my name would be Sam.

On the Saturday I decided to meet Kate outside the Church in Dominick Street. I was dressed as usual in a suit. I had made a special effort to look my best, I was a little apprehensive as I waited, it was my first time to meet a girl on my own. I wondered if she would show up. After what seemed like an hour Kate came walking along with Annie.

"Hello, fancy meeting you here," Annie said. I must have looked confused. I said, "I thought I was to meet Kate here today." My face turned red with embarrassment. They both smiled.

Annie said, "It's ok I'm only walking down to the shops. You two enjoy yourselves," Annie said as she walked away. I felt relieved watching Annie walk away. I turned to Kate she was still smiling.

"So, how are you?," I asked.

"I'm great, you are looking well," she said.

"You look lovely what would you like to do?" I asked.

"Let's just walk a while, see where we end up," said Kate. "There's a lovely park up towards Phibsboro, we could go up that way," I said. "Ok, let's go."

It was a beautiful Autumn Day the leaves just starting to turn a lovely orange colour. "So, Sam tell me about yourself?" Kate asked. While walking up Stoneybatter we began to learn about each other.

"You seem very shy around girls, yet your also very confident in yourself," Kate said. "I am not used to being with girls, in fact I don't know how I got the nerve to ask you out!"

"Well, I'm glad you did," she answered. It was the first time in my life I ever spoke so easy to someone not in my family. Time passed so quickly; we were at the park before we knew. There was a tearoom near the gate.

"Would you like a cup of tea," I asked.

"That would be nice," she answered. We went in and ordered tea and they had lovely cream buns, sitting there I couldn't take my eyes off her. She was beautiful, she had the biggest brown eyes and dark auburn hair. I got embarrassed when she caught me watching her. I started to ask her about her family just to have her talk. She was from a family of six, one brother and five sisters. Her father and brother were painters. She was the third child in the family. Her brother Jonnie and her uncles had been in WW1 in the British Army. One uncle was killed in the war. I told her about my family. Before long, it was time to go home. As we walked along, she took my hand, it felt so right just rambling along side by side.

"What do you think of the situation we are in here?" I asked.

"What do you mean? The War?" She asked.

"Yeah you know like the way things are, seeing your family were in the British Army."

"Why would you want to know about that, not very romantic on our first date."

"Ye see I feel I can talk to you more than anyone else I know, other than my brother Christy. I feel I could say anything to you."

"Well to answer your question, I was born here and live here seeing the way we are treated in our own country is wrong. I am an Irish woman. We should be a free country," Kate said, "Does that answer your question?"

"Yes, that answers my question, because I have to tell you I am involved with the Volunteers." Kate looked up at me with a wry smile, "I thought as much, you are a bit too sure of yourself to be just a builders apprentice," she said.

"I just thought you should know in case you felt different about it," I said.

"Ok let's forget about the war, we will just think about being young and together for now," she said.

"You know my cousin Annie?"

"Of course I do, she's my dance teacher."

"Well she is going to marry a fellow called Tommy Bryan. Do you know him? He is one of the Volunteers. She met him a while ago, he's from down around Henrietta Street, a good-looking fella."

"I have heard the name, but I don't know him, he is in a different company," I answered. "Well they are getting married soon, Annie was saying I am going to be her bridesmaid! Won't that be nice."

"Yes, I am sure you would be great," I said. When we reached the corner where she lived Kate said, "that was a lovely day I enjoyed myself."

"Me too, I hope we can do it again," I said. With that she went up on her toes and kissed my cheek. She only reached up to my shoulder. "I have to go. I'll see you again said Kate." I stood and watched till she reached the doorway and disappeared into the house. Walking home my emotions were all over the place, walking down Capel Street and an army lorry swept by, probably on its way to the castle which brought me back to earth in a hurry.

Chapter 11
Bloody Sunday

I began meeting with Kate whenever we got the opportunity. We went to the cinema and saw some funny films, other times we walked and talked and enjoyed each other's company. One evening on our way up to Kate's house we ran into a checkpoint. It was manned by Auxiliary and DMP. There was no way to avoid it without bringing notice to ourselves. Kate squeezed my hand as we approached the Police. The soldiers were just standing back as the Police asked the questions. Fortunately, the Police didn't have their hearts in it, they were passing most people through without too much of a fuss.

The soldiers for the most part just lounged against their cars watching. When it was Kate's turn to go through the policeman just waved her on, of course the soldiers started making lewd remarks as she passed by. A couple of the soldiers walked over and blocked her path, while the looked her up and down. "What do you think Bill, maybe this one is hiding something," licking his lips in a suggestive way. Kate just stood saying nothing. In the meantime, the policeman gave me a quick search and passed me on. As I came level with Kate, I took her arm to carry on.

"Where do you think you're going," the soldier asked.

"We are on our way home," I said.

"Is that so?" said the soldier.

"We might have other plans for you!" He said in a threatening manner. Inside I was raging, if I had a gun in my pocket, I would have used it on this soldier. Just his slimy attitude made my skin crawl. The DMP constable walked over.

"Come on move along we have enough to be doing this evening," with that he gave us the opportunity to get past. We hurried away; it was all I could do not to look back at that soldier. As the saying goes if looks could kill.

"Are you OK Kate," I asked. "I am fine, you get used to it. I try to ignore them, it's the only way?"

"I could have killed him for the way he looked at you," I said.

"It's OK, I'll be all right especially when I am with you!" Kate said. When we arrived at Kate's house, I walked her into the hall. There was no one about. It was starting to get dark. I took her in my arms and held her. I could feel my passion rising as she looked up at me. I kissed her soft lips and she melted in my arms. We were oblivious to all around us for a few minutes. Then the sounds of people moving about on the stairs broke the spell. I felt an emotion I had never experienced before. I was bursting inside with a kind of love that was new to me. I never felt like this about anyone before.

"I think I am in love with you, Kate," I said with her head leaning against my chest she said, "I know, I feel the same way too. I better go up, it's getting late. You should get going too."

Just as I was about to leave two women came up the steps into the gloom of the hall, they were chatting not minding us then this lady said, "Kitty who's this you are with?"

"Ooh! Mammy this is my friend Sam."

"Well now it's nice to meet you, Sam."

"Hello Mrs Glynn," I said. "Bring him up to say hello to the rest of the family, we can have a cup of tea," Kate's mam said. Kate took my hand, and we went up the stairs to their flat. These houses had no lighting in the staircase areas, so they tended to be very dark. When we went into the flat it was very cosy with a lovely fire going and the oil lamps gave it a warm glow.

"Come in," said Kate's mother, "sit yourself down and we have a cup of tea."

Mrs Glynn was lovely woman with a ruddy complexion and very friendly. There were two sisters and her father in the room, the girls were younger than Kate. They just looked up from what they were doing and almost whispered Hello. Her Dad was sitting by the fire smoking a pipe with his feet up,

"Who's this fella?" Kate's Dad asked.

"This is Kate's friend; he just came up to say hello. I was just going to make tea."

"Hello," the dad said.

"Nice to meet you sir," I said. "There're no sirs in this house, my name is John."

I am sure Kate was embarrassed it's always a bit awkward in these situations. We just made some small talk I didn't give up too much information other than to say where our family lived. Soon it was time to leave. "Thanks for the tea Mam, it was lovely and goodnight all," I said as I left. Kate saw me out to the landing. She was blushing and smiling. "Well at least they know who my boyfriend is." I gave her a cuddle and left.

By the end of October Michael Collins was fuming. Kevin Barry had been sentenced to be hung for murder for his part in the Monk's Bakery attack. People had expected his sentence to be commuted to life imprisonment on account of his young age 18. But unfortunately, one of the soldiers killed in the action was only 17 so the sentence remained death by hanging. There had been a huge protest outside Mountjoy with thousands of people praying the Rosary.

Collins had toyed with trying to rescue Barry using the Squad, but a feasible plan was not produced. As the week went by things were hotting up, plans were in the works for an all-out offensive against the British Intelligence unit in the Castle, 'The Cairo gang'. It was going to happen on Sunday the 20th of November. It was a large operation involving the elite members of 'The Squad', these were the handpicked men of the ASU who were responsible for carrying out the orders of Michael Collins in eliminating known informers and detectives from the Castle. My unit was to join The Squad with help from different units from the Dublin Brigade as we needed a large group of men to execute the plan.

Different members of the Squad led teams that were tasked with finding and executing individuals in different areas of the city. The plan was for all the teams to strike simultaneously all over the city to shoot the Intelligence officers involved. We had gathered information on the whereabouts of these men from all kinds of sources. We were going to attack early on the Sunday morning. There was a lot of activity on the Saturday as we prepared for the attack. That evening I felt very apprehensive.

I walked home from HQ armed with a parabellum automatic, it felt extra heavy in my pocket not knowing what tomorrow would bring. As I passed my local Church on Halston St I had the urge to go in and say a prayer. Now, I wouldn't be overly religious, but I just needed to sit quietly and reflect. I would be involved tomorrow in what some people considered to be murder, as a young lad my feelings were all over the place. To shoot somebody in battle is what I had been trained for, to execute someone in cold blood was an unknown to me.

I had to think if I would be able to do my duty as required. Sitting in the quiet of the Church I remembered all I had seen and experienced in the few years I have been around. The tragic history of our country and the savage price our people have paid to try to throw off the English yoke. I made my peace, said a prayer and left the church knowing that I would do whatever was needed.

Sunday morning broke as a bright day with sunshine with white fluffy clouds scudding across a pale blue sky. I had been assigned to Vinny Byrnes section; we were assigned to an address on Mount Street on the south side of the city. There were about eight of us, four would enter the dwellings and four cover the outside. We were to meet up in Westland Row outside the Church. Some of the men went to early mass and we met outside after mass at 9 o'clock. We spread out and walked towards our assigned target. When we arrived at our destination our section leader Vinny said, "Set up our cover, two men at the steps leading to the hall door. Two men across the street watching the road."

Four of us walked up to the door, we knocked on the door as the maid answered the door. We brushed past her and told her to go to the kitchen. When she saw our weapons, she panicked and ran screaming into the kitchen. We raced up the stairs to the room where we should find the Intelligence officers. I was the last man in, giving cover to the others. As our men burst through the door into the bedroom a man started to rise, there was warning shout and another man appeared on the next landing brandishing a revolver. He started to aim at us, instinct took over and I fired twice hitting him in the chest, the report from the shots in the staircase was deafening.

He fell down the stairs landing close by us. Vinny Byrne gave the officer in the room a moment and told him to say his prayers. Then he and our other man fired killing the man. The shock of the man falling down the stairs and sight of the wounds unnerved me momentarily. The other men started moving to run down the stairs. Vinny grabbed me by the collar of my coat and shoved me down the stairs. "Come on move yerself we have to get going," Vinny shouted at me.

As we reached the street, we could hear gunfire coming from Haddington Road. We started to walk quickly towards the canal. Beggars Bush Barracks, the HQ of the Auxiliaries, is based close by. As we crossed the road, we could hear the sound of engines starting up in the Barracks.

"OK lads. Scatter, head for the Quays, it's our best way out. Follow me Sam and keep moving, this could get ugly fast," Vinny said.

We made it to the other side of the canal out of Mount St Once there we could go down the back lanes without being seen. There was a running battle happening close by as we could hear the firing. Some of our other units were engaging soldiers on another street. On Sunday morning there weren't many people about, so we had no chance of hiding in a crowd. Luckily, we managed to get down to the river, there's a ferry the dockers use at the Ferryman's Inn to cross the river as the closest bridge is a good distance away. If he was on the south side, we could escape quickly.

Fortunately, the ferry was at the South wall when we got there, in the distance we could still hear the odd gun shot. We climbed down the ladder to the platform. The operator said, "I'll be leavin' in 10 Minutes."

The three of us got in the boat. Vinny looked at the man and said, "You will be leavin' now," as he spoke, he opened his coat to reveal his gun.

The operator swallowed and replied, "Certainly Sir, immediate departure," and cast-off rowing us across to safety. Climbing out of the boat at the North wall Vinny handed the Ferryman ten bob note. "Thanks," he said.

The ferryman lifted his cap in salute once across we would have the time to make a clean getaway.

As I walked along the Quays there were lots of people coming from the city centre. There was a GAA football match due to be played in Croke Park not far from where we landed on the North Wall. Dublin was to play Tipperary in a challenge match. Groups of people were heading down to the park. There were a lot of supporters from Tipperary who had come up for the game. It wouldn't be long before the Army, Tans, and the Auxiliary's were out in force looking for us, and lots of people on the streets didn't bode well.

I tried to be as inconspicuous as possible. But you just got the feeling that this was not going to be any ordinary day. My mind was all over the place, I kept thinking about the shooting of the soldiers. I had never witnessed a killing so close up and seen the spray of blood and the sound of the impact of the bullets. It would be a while before I would forget it. Most of the action had taken place on the South side of the city, so mostly it was DMP police officers that were in the vicinity where we landed. They were busy controlling the flow of people towards Croke Park. I made my way home to our house.

When I got home the house was empty, Mam and Dinah were at mass. I had a wash and changed my clothes. I hid my weapon in a hole in the wall behind our house, it was a good spot not easily found. I was supposed to meet up with

Kate that afternoon, we had arranged to go to the pictures. Just as I finished Mam and Dinah came in, "Hello," Mam said, "we weren't expecting to see you so early. Is everything all right. I thought you were playing a match today."

"No, the game was cancelled on account of the big game at Croke Park," I said, "I am going out later."

"Do you want some breakfast?" Dinah asked.

"Yeah, I'll have some if it's going."

Dinah got busy making tea and frying sausages and eggs. I hadn't realised how hungry I was. When I was finished, I checked outside, so far no activity in our area. "Ok Ma I am heading out I will see you later ok."

I put on my topcoat and started walking over to Dominick St I got as far as Parnell Street when the first of a group of army lorries passed by, they were driving fast heading towards O'Connell St. The picture house we were going to was in Mary St so we should be all right. Trying to keep things as normal as possible was a lot harder than I thought it would be. In order to function you had to try to separate the army from your daily life, keeping as normal as possible routine to avoid detection. Being young was an advantage as I was inclined to be impulsive and able to live in the moment. So, by the time I met up with Kate I felt more relaxed. Kate was waiting outside her house, she looked great all dressed up being Sunday.

"Hello, you look smashing," I said.

She just gave me a smile, "You probably say that to all the girls," she said. "So where are we off too?" She asked.

"There's a Charlie Chaplin picture on at the Plaza. Is that ok?" I asked.

"Good. Let's go," she said. We walked arm in arm down to Mary St and went into the Pictures. It felt good to be sitting in the dark close to someone you cared for deeply. We were lost in our own little world enjoying each other's company.

As we left the theatre you could feel the tension in the air. People were hurrying home everyone seemed in a hurry. I asked a man passing by, "What's going on?"

"There's been murder in Croke Park, the Tans and the army are after shooting into the crowd, loads of people were killed or wounded," he said. "The army are all over the place, ye better get home."

"Ok Kate, let's go," I said. As we started off, we could see there was panic in the streets. We tried to go towards Dominick St, but the roads were blocked by the Police. "Let's go down to Capel Street, maybe we can go back up that way."

Next thing we heard engine's roaring, an armoured car and lorry load of soldiers heading down to the Quays. We dodged into a doorway away from view just in case. Kate was terrified by this time. There's a place I know where we can stay till it quiet's down. We headed up Mary St and turned on to Stafford St there was a house we used as a safe house. We went in and up the stairs to a room on the top landing. I found the key in its usual hiding place; I had used this room before to hide.

The room was basic, a table two chairs and a kind of couch you could sleep on. It felt cold and damp, there was a fireplace and a few logs. "How do you know this place?" asked Kate.

"It belongs to one of our men. He is in Mountjoy so we can use it when we need to. We have a few places to lie low when necessary. I'll see if I can light the fire it will warm us up," I said. I was able to light a few sticks and before long we had a little fire going.

"Why do you think the Army attacked Croke Park," Kate asked. Looking at her I knew I would have to answer truthfully.

"They are retaliating for an operation we carried out against their men," I answered. "Were you involved?"

"Yes, I was there."

"My God was this today?" Kate asked.

"Early this morning," I said. "I can't believe you were out this morning killing people, and then came up to see me to go out!" She said. Her face had lost all its colour and she was starting to shiver. I walked over to her, put my arms around her. I just held her, feeling her shaking in my arms.

"I'm sorry but It's what we had to do. I had no choice, none of us have! It's War. They would shoot us without any thought if they got the chance."

"How can you do it, you are only a kid."

"I am a soldier just as they are. But this is my country, and we are fighting for our freedom," I answered. "I had to shoot a man today and if I hadn't reacted just a fraction faster than him, I would not be here now. I didn't enjoy it but what could I do." Kate fell against my chest, she was crying. "Stop crying Kate," I said, "I am sorry if I upset you."

"I just realised you might have been killed today," Kate said.

"I couldn't handle that; I am in love with you." When we kissed, we both knew that nothing would break us apart. We sat on the couch and before we knew we were aroused, and I started to pull back, but Kate held me and said, "I want you to love me now! We may never have another chance who knows what will happen."

"I'm not sure, you are my first girlfriend," I said.

"You will be my first and only love," said Kate. All our inhibitions disappeared, and we made love for the first time. The bond between us became unbreakable, and we both knew we would always be together no matter what!

By evening time things had quieted down, we sat holding each other just watching the fire die down. We could hear people moving about in other parts of the house it broke the spell. "I better try to get you home now," I said.

"I would love to stay here, but I can't I have to go home," Kate answered. We made sure the fire was safe and started down the stairs. Once in the street it was quiet. It was already dark. We walked up Parnell Street, there were lots of police on the way watching for trouble. At the corner of Dominick Street, a DMP officer stopped us.

"Where are you going?" He asked.

"We are just going home, I live up there," said Kate.

"Well," he said, "get along with ye it's not a night to be on the streets."

As we reached Kate's house her mother was in the Hallway. "Where in the name of God have you been? I was worried sick," she said.

"I'm sorry Mammy, we were at the Pictures and when we came out the streets were blocked off; we couldn't get by." Her mam said, "We were worried sick. All kinds of thing have been happening today. Thank God your back now. The Army have been raiding all over the city looking for IRA men." As she spoke, she gave me a knowing look. "It might be better if you stayed here for a while, the streets tonight are very dangerous."

"Thank you, Mrs Glynn, but I'll be OK. I know my way around," I answered.

"I am sure you do," said Mrs Glynn. "Kate don't delay down here," Mrs Glynn said as she started up the stairs. Kate gave me a hug. "You be careful I will be worried about you."

"Don't worry I'll be all right," I kissed her passionately. As I walked out into the dark street, I wondered what lay ahead. I had crossed so many lines on this day. I was no longer a youth I was a man and a soldier.

Chapter 12
Conflict Within

When I got back to our house Mam and Dinah were out which was unusual as they seldom went out at night. I went over to Uncle Jerrys; he was sitting by the fire when I went in. "Sam it's good to see you, are you OK? Terrible business today!"

"What do you mean?" I asked "What's wrong?"

"There was a big attack by the IRA this morning and several soldiers and officers killed in different parts of the city. Then the Tans went Mad! Did you not hear about young Willie Robinson, your cousin, was shot today in Croke Park there was a lot of people killed and injured? He's in a bad way in the hospital. Your Mam and Dinah went up too Little Britain Street to see the family."

"No, I didn't know, the roads were all blocked off. I had to wait till things died down to come home."

"Well," said Uncle Jerry, "I was told the Army and the Tans surrounded Croke Park and fired into the crowd. They killed quite a few of the spectators and some of the players, no one knows for sure what happened. It's an awful thing! The women went to see Willie's family then they are going to the church, they should be home soon."

I couldn't believe my ears, to think that soldiers would shoot into an innocent crowd at a football match. This was the worst atrocity that had yet happened. I felt sick to think that I had been part of the attack that had caused this tragedy. I knew young Willie, he lived not far from us. His father and mine were brothers, he would sometimes come and watch us playing football down in the Square. Standing there in my Uncle's house I was overcome with grief to realise my actions had led to this. I must have turned white, Jerry came over, "Sit down

Sam." I sat on a chair at the table, Uncle Jerry came over with a drink. "Here take this it looks like you need it," he said.

I put the glass to my mouth and took a swallow, the sensation of burning in my mouth and down to my stomach woke me from my stupor. "My God what was that?"

"A drop of the creature. I keep for medicinal purposes. You looked like you needed it."

"Thanks. I did. I better go." With the taste of the drink still burning in my belly I left to go home.

There was still lots of activity on the streets. You could hear the sound of cars and armoured cars rushing through the streets. There would be raids looking for us all over the city. There was no chance of getting to a safe house with all the activity, so I had to hope my house was not on the list. I went to the back yard and took my gun from its hiding place and made sure it was ready for use just in case. Having a weapon gave me a sense of security, at least if worst came to worst, I would have a fighting chance. I put the gun under my pillow and went into the parlour. When Mam and Dinah came in, I was sitting by the fire making a cup of tea.

"Sam, you are home safe. Thank God!" Mam said. "I am sure you heard about your cousin."

"Yes, Uncle Jerry just told me. How is young Willie?" I asked.

"He is not doing very well. His Family are devastated. God help them. He is in Jervis Street Hospital. We went and said some prayers for him in Halston St He's in God's hands now," Mam said.

"Is Christy in?" She asked.

"I haven't seen him today," I answered. "I hope he was not involved in all that happened today," she said. I couldn't say anything I was still wrestling with my emotions and did not want to start a conversation that might get her upset. I made the tea and sat at the fire then I made an excuse to go lie down. I opened the window. I would be able to hear any activity and I could get into the back yard quickly. As soon as I lay down the events of the day started to roll around in my head. I just lay in the dark thinking of all I had experienced in one day. As if I had lived a lifetime in one day. It was going to be a long night.

The following morning, I rose early after a fitful sleep. Mam was already had a pot boiling on the fire. This was normal as the fish market did not open on Mondays. "Sit down I am making some tea," she said.

"That was a terrible shock hearing about young Willie, his poor mother and father are in bits. I was picturing myself in the same situation It could have been one of you."

"I know it's not easy Ma, but we have to keep fighting otherwise it's all for nothing," I said.

"Yes! I know, but it doesn't get any easier when your children are constantly on the run, your still only boys to me. A mammy shouldn't have to bury her child."

"Don't worry Ma we are being very careful," I said. "Do you want something to eat? I'll make some porridge, it'll do you good," Ma said. Dinah came into the room and sat with us we had our breakfast each with our own thoughts. As I was ready to leave Ma came over to me hugged me. "Be careful and look after that brother of yours."

"I will, Ma. I will be back when I can." With that I left feeling sombre but ready for what the day might bring. The next morning broke with some terrible news, two of the commanders of the ASU had been captured, Dick Mc Kee and Pleader Clancy. They were captured along with another man Conor Clune. They had been taken to the Castle. They had been horribly tortured and bayonetted and finally 'Shot trying to escape'. It sent shock waves through our organisation. The loss of these men took its toll on all of us. I also learned that my cousin Willie had also died of his wounds.

The family were grieving such a tragic loss. I went into the market to see my Ma, as it was safer to talk to my Ma there. I didn't want to bring attention to our house. She was terribly upset about young Willie only 11 years old he was being buried the following day and she and most of the family would attend. We had to lie low to avoid detection.

It took a few weeks for things to die down. I had been moving around from place to place occasionally visiting my mother to reassure her I was ok. It was December and nearing the Christmas holidays. Our unit were constantly on the watch for Tan or police activity. A few lads had been picked up and questioned and released after interrogation. So far, I had been lucky but the stress of constantly being on edge was hard and I felt tired. Kate was my only solace when I was with her, I felt more relaxed. We managed to meet up every few days. Dominick Street was a busy area with lots of families living in the tenements. So being around there I was less conspicuous.

One evening as we came back to Kate's house her mam again invited me in, sitting chatting time flew by. It was Christmas week, so people were looking forward to the festivities in spite of all that had happened in the last month. When I was leaving a group of young girls and boys had gathered on the landing and on the stairs, they were telling ghost stories and having a laugh. All of a sudden, they started to scatter. A patrol of Auxiliary's had crept into the buildings they were wearing tennis shoes so their boots would not make noise and give them away.

One of them shouted at the kids on the stairs. Kate and I ran back into her mam's flat closing the door. "What's wrong?" Mrs Glynn asked.

"There's soldiers in the building," Kate said. You could hear the commotion as soldiers charged up the stairs shouting at the fleeing children. Mrs Glynn knew by me I was worried I didn't want to put anyone in danger with my presence. I wasn't armed so if they came in, I might be able to talk my way out. We heard banging on doors as the soldiers tried to gain access to some of the flats. Mr Glynn stood up as the door was being hammered on.

"I'll talk to these fellas," he said. Opening the door, there was a Sergeant with another soldier with a fixed bayonet.

"What do you want? You are disturbing my family," he said.

"Who's in here?" Demanded the sergeant.

"My family," said Mr Glynn, "and they are no concern of yours. We are a peaceful family. I wore that uniform before you ever did. I took a bullet for the Queen at Lindley in the Boer War. So, leave us alone you have no business here." The soldiers were flabbergasted and embarrassed.

"Sorry to bother you," the sergeant said moving away quickly. Mr Glynn closed the door and leaned back on the door. "I think I need a drink after that."

"I think you deserve one," said Mrs Glynn reaching up on a shelf that held a bottle of whiskey. Mrs Glynn poured a generous measure into a cup and gave it to him. He downed it with relish. "That was close" he said looking at me, "it might be a good idea if you stayed here tonight, them fellas will be around for a while. You can use my chair; I'm going to lie down." It had been a close call. I spent a long night stoking the fire and trying to sleep knowing Kate slept a few feet away.

Christmas Day arrived people were out and about it was a bright crisp day, going to Mass and visiting friends and family. The streets were quiet enough soldiers were keeping a low profile. Christy and I spent Christmas Eve at home with the family. Molly now had a Fiancé Mark, whom we knew was a member of the 1st Battalion. They planned to marry, in February. After Mass we all came back to our house for dinner. Uncle Jerry joined us, and we had a lovely time, almost normal, there was always an undercurrent of tension knowing anything could happen. It was as close to a normal Christmas as we could have.

Mam was delighted to have us all around and looked happy. On St Stephens Day as soon as I could make my excuses, I headed for Dominick Street. I was looking forward to seeing Kate, we were going to the Theatre Royal for a show. I got to Kate's house and was invited in. I was now almost part of the family. After tasting the Christmas pudding, a family tradition and a glass of stout; we were able to leave for the show. It was our first Christmas together and we just wanted to be on our own. It felt so good just to be able to walk hand in hand, we were lost in our own world. As we walked down O'Connell St, we came to the Gresham Hotel one of Dublin's finest.

I guided Kate up the stairs to the door. "What's going on?" Kate asked.

"I thought we could have some tea as it is Christmas," I answered.

"Are you Mad! They won't let us in," said Kate.

"Don't worry, they don't turn away paying customers." I said. We went through to the Grand Foyer. At the Salon, the man at the door greeted us and showed us to a table.

"Your waiter will be with you shortly," he said. Kate was taken in by the opulence of the place.

"I thought you deserved a treat seeing that it is Christmas!" I said.

"Thank you it's beautiful. I am not sure I am properly dressed for such a posh place," Kate answered.

"You most certainly are, you are beautiful so sit back and enjoy. It's my first time here also." It was great to sit in comfort and enjoy being together just like ordinary people. We were served a lovely afternoon tea and even had a glass of sherry to mark the occasion. By the time we walked over to the Royal all our anxiety was gone. The show was very enjoyable I think Kate floated home she was so taken by our day out. Leaving her at her house I wished things were different but knowing the uncertainty of the times reality would soon change our lives.

Chapter 13
A New Year

The new year started off quiet enough, I was involved in training and surveillance. We were watching the Castle; we would follow possible agents and trace their movements. We heard that there had been peace feeler's out by an archbishop Clune from Australia he was related to Conor Clune murdered on Bloody Sunday with Dick Mc Kee and Peadar Clancy. People were weary of war, but they still supported an Irish Republic. Things were still happening in the country. Cork had been taken the brunt of atrocities at the start of the new year. There were ambushes by the Flying Column's which caused casualty among the Tans and Auxiliary's, who in turn committed reprisals against the ordinary people.

On the 21st of January I also learned about an ambush in Drumcondra that went wrong. H company of the 1st battalion had tried to set up an ambush at Binn's Bridge at the Royal Canal. Somehow the ambush was moved to Tolka Bridge in Drumcondra. When the ambush began our soldiers were out gunned and should have withdrawn. A firefight ensued which was disastrous for our side with one killed and four captured. Tommy Bryan was the one captured man.

The others managed to get away across the fields. How was I going to break the news to Kate? That evening when I arrived at Dominick St the news had preceded me, there was an ominous feeling in the air. Annie and Tommy had been married a couple of months previously and they were expecting their first child. Kate's mother told me Kate was down at Annie's place in Henrietta St I said I would see her later as I didn't want to intrude in this situation. It was sobering thought walking back to my safe house in Stafford Street.

While walking I noticed a man following me. I crossed the road and loitered looking in a shop window to see if he carried on. The man had stopped and was still watching me. I cut Down Little Mary St I entered into number 25 This was a place I knew there was a way out under the house. I ran down the hall and opened the door to the cellar. I entered the cellar it was very dark, and I had to light a match to see. I closed the door from the inside and went through the cellar, the wall in the foundation had an opening that went underneath the street through an old sewer and came out several houses down on the opposite side of the street.

As I emerged, I spotted the man who must have been a detective going into number 25. As soon as he went in, I headed up Mary Street and went to the safe house on Stafford Street. I would hold up there for a few days. I would have to talk to Kate later. This was a lesson to keep up my guard. I just hoped he didn't know where I lived. Which would put my family in danger. I would have to be extra careful.

In early January of 1921 I was told to report to Paddy Daly at HQ. "Hello," Sam Daly said, " You are being assigned to the Squad; as of now, you know we had a few men captured and killed so you will now we need some extra men."

"Yes sir I will do my best," I answered.

"You will be with Tom Keogh for now. Just carry on you will be given jobs as needed."

"Yes Sir," I answered.

A couple of days later I met up with Kate, she told me about Annie and was worried the same fate was in store for me. "Where are you staying now?" she asked. I told her I was moving around a bit just in case.

"Don't be worrying I am being very careful." I neglected to mention being followed, it wouldn't do any good for her to know.

Another of these ambushes took place in February up in Longford, a spectacular attack on the Forces in the area by Sean Mac Eoin the commander of the Longford brigade which saw the IRA defeat a large RIC and Military force. He was known as the Blacksmith of Ballina Lee and became one of the most able of brigade commanders.

As the month went by, we learned that Tommy Bryan along with three other Volunteers had been tried and found guilty of treason against the crown and were sentenced to die by hanging. Needless to say, this was terrible news for the Glynn family. I went to see Kate. "I can't believe they are going to hang Tommy! It will be the death of Annie," Kate said, "She is in an awful state."

What could I say to make things better? I was only doing exactly the same things Tommy had been doing. "God help them both. Kate said I will help her as much as I can. I am going up to Mountjoy prison with Annie to see Tommy next Friday."

"I could bring you up to the prison," Sam said, "I can wait outside and bring you home."

"Are you sure is it not dangerous for you? Kate asked. We can take a hackney, a friend of mine has one and there will be loads of people around so it will be ok," said Sam. When the Friday came Kate and a heavily pregnant Annie, the baby due in April, went to the prison. My friend Charlie drove us in his hackney. I watched as they went through the small entrance. I would wait till they came out to take them home.

Kate linked Annie passing through the gate. There were lots of people about, some protesting the sentences of the doomed and others praying for them. It was a harrowing experience for them knowing that time was running out. Tommy was to be executed on the 14th of March along with three others. The warders were sympathetic when the saw Annie's condition and led them through to a room set aside for visits. When Tommy saw them, he said, "Now no tears in front of these Tans. We have to be strong."

They were not allowed to hold each other. Trying to have a conversation was difficult with armed guards lining the walls. The visit only lasted an hour but felt longer. The smells and the whole feeling of the place was repulsive. Annie was very pale and anxious, as the visit ended. "We will be here next week," Annie said. Tommy stood and smiled at us giving us a wink as we left. "Don't forget to tell the baby all about his Daddy."

As they left Tommy started to sing to Annie, "It's only a step from Killarney to Heaven."

His sweet voice reverberating around the corridor as we walked. I thought Annie was going to collapse. Tears now flowed down her cheeks as we made our way through the prison. It was impossible to remain strong knowing it would be the last time they would be together. Kate had to support Annie down to the prison gate. as soon as we were out of the prison, she broke down completely it was so hard to keep it all in, especially in her condition. Sam saw us coming out of the gate and hurried over to help us. Between us we managed to get Annie into the hackney.

I was glad to leave Mountjoy behind. "I am going to stay with Annie tonight," said Kate.

"No problem," said Sam he took them to Henrietta St and left. The following day Sam was shocked to learn that Annie's baby had been stillborn through the night. Luckily Kate had stayed and had been able to help with some other women to get Annie to the Rotunda Hospital where the baby was stillborn, the stress had taken its toll on poor Annie. On the morning of March 14th 1921 the hangman brought Tommy's young life to an end along with his comrades. They were executed in Pairs at 2-hour intervals six men died that morning. The cruelty of the regime knew no bounds in the early hours of. a huge crowd had gathered outside the prison to Pray for the men and to protest this aberration. His family had asked for the body but were refused; the executed men were to be buried within the walls of the prison and buried in quick lime. It was no wonder people ended up hating the British establishment.

Chapter 14
The Proposal

It was a tough time for the ASU, the murder in our eyes of six of our comrades left a bitter taste on our tongues. I had been busy with different assignments, and it was about a couple of days after I met up with Kate. Saint Patricks Day was the following day. I met her as usual at her house. It was a pleasant enough evening and I thought we could go for a walk. While we walked Kate seemed distant and distracted. "Are you OK Kate?," I asked. With that she started to cry. My first reaction was she had such a traumatic time with Annie. "Is this because of what happened with Annie?" I asked.

"No, it's not about Annie. It's about me and you."

"I am not sure what you mean," I answered. "I think I am pregnant."

I reached out and took both her hands in mine and looking her in the eyes I said, "I love you. I am here for you and I will look after you. It's OK, sure we were always going to get married." Sam said. It will just be a bit sooner that's all. Kate threw her arms around my neck and held me like there was no tomorrow.

"But what about our families," she said.

"We will deal with all of that as it happens. Just know we are meant to be together and no one else matters. We will manage on our own if we have to."

We walked home to Kates, she felt better having told me. "What are you going to say to your Mam?"

"I will have to tell her the truth, I am pregnant, and we are getting married!" I left Kate at the front door, we both needed time to sort things out.

I gave her a kiss and held her. "I'll see you tomorrow OK, everything will be alright. Don't worry," I said. I watched as she climbed the stairs to her flat understanding the way she felt.

Needless to say, on my way back from Kates my mind was occupied with the situation I found myself in. I needed someone to talk to, I went in search of Christy. I eventually found him at Aunt Mary's house in Little Strand Street. We had both been moving around due to operations we were involved in. Aunt Mary answered the door to me. "Is Christy here?" I asked.

"Yes, come on in he's upstairs."

As soon as she had the door closed Mary asked, "Is everything alright? I heard about young Tommy Bryan and the others. Lord have Mercy on them, a terrible business."

"Yes, it was awful for his wife. She's Kate's first cousin. They went to the prison together to see him the night before," I told her.

"God! What an awful experience that must have been," she said. Christy came down the stairs "Howaya Sam?"

"Okay. You?" I answered.

"Yeah, you know how it is." We couldn't talk about what we were doing when there was anyone else around. It was dangerous for them and for us. Aunt Mary sensed we wanted some privacy. "OK I'll let you fellas talk, do you need to stay tonight, Sam?"

"Yes, if that's OK?" I answered. "Of course, it will be a tight squeeze with three of you," she said. We were to share a bed with her young son Kevin.

When Mary went upstairs, we went out into the back yard to talk. "So, what's up?" asked Christy.

"I am going to get married. Kate is expecting a baby. I just needed to talk to someone!" I said.

"Jaysus! You're only a kid! When did all this happen?," Christy asked.

"Around the time of Bloody Sunday, we were together, and it just happened. By the way I'm not a kid, I'm a man."

"Sorry I didn't mean it like that. Have you told anyone else?" asked Christy.

"No, I only found out today but I'm not sorry. I love Kate and we were always going to get married, so now it will be sooner than I thought."

"Well now how are you going to tell Ma? She'll have a fit," Christy said.

"I will tell her as soon as possible. It would be good if you could be there," I said.

"I will make sure I am, Kate is a lovely girl, she will be a great wife. Just things are so uncertain at the moment it will be hard for everybody involved."

"Yes, I know, look what happened with Annie Bryan her baby was stillborn, it was a terrible shock for Kate. But she understands the situation we're in, she knows that any day it could be me or you caught or killed. She still wants to be with me, and I want to be with her," I said. "Ok we will go talk to Ma tomorrow."

With that Christy put out his hand, we shook hands and he said, "I am happy for you little brother," giving me a big hug. It felt so good to share my thoughts with Christy.

Saint Patricks Day dawned, it was a day off for most people and a holy day, so everybody went to mass. Christy and I met Ma and Dinah walking home from mass. Women's intuition took over, Ma guessed something was up. "Is everything all right," she asked as we met.

"Yeah," I answered "I just need to talk to you."

"Ok we'll go home and have some breakfast," said Mam. When we arrived at the house Dinah busied herself preparing breakfast. "So, what is going on?" Ma asked.

Standing up and taking a deep breath I began. "I am going to get married," I said.

"You're WHAT!" Mam said.

"I am getting married," I repeated.

"And what brought this on? Who is this girl?" said Ma, her voice rising becoming animated.

"Her name is Kate Glynn and we have been going out for almost a year. Kate is expecting our baby."

"Oh my God. I didn't know you were even seeing a girl, how come you never brought her around?"

"Mam these are not normal circumstances. I'm sorry but Kate and I are in love, living day by day not knowing what was in store. Seeing my friends die and injured, being on the run has changed me. I am no longer a little boy, I am a man, and I am in love, and I will stand by Kate."

Mam sat down at the table, her head in her hands. It was a while before she spoke. "Does this girl's family know?" Mam asked.

"Kate was going to tell her Mam and Dad today," I answered.

"Where is this Kate from?" Mam asked.

"Her family are from Dominick Street. Her dad is a painter/decorator, they are a nice family."

"Well, if the girl is expecting what can we do, you have to marry her. I don't believe this. You are so young!" Mam said.

"I know I am of a young age, but I am not a kid. I had to grow up fast like so many more of my friends. Some of whom are not around anymore. Kate knows the way things are and she is prepared for what might or might not happen. Her cousin's husband was hanged last month in Mountjoy, Kate was with Annie visiting the night before he was hung. So, she is a strong person."

"The poor girl!" Mam said. Looking at Christy Mam asked, "Did you know about this?"

"No, I didn't. I knew he went out with someone, but I have only met Kate a few months ago."

"Well, we will have to look after this girl but don't expect me to over the moon about it, it's not the way a mother wants to learn about a marriage."

"Thank you, Mam," again I said, "I am sorry about the way this happened, but I am happy to marry Kate. When I bring her around to meet you, you will understand."

Kate was at mass with her mother and sisters on the same morning. While walking home Kate asked her Mam to talk to her alone. Her Mam sent the younger girl's home with Sarah, making an excuse to go get the newspaper. As they walked along Kate told her mother she was expecting a baby. Although shocked, she was not surprised. "What's going to happen?" Asked her Mam.

"Sam is telling his mother today as well, and we are going to get married."

"Your Dad will be very disappointed with you," said Mam. "I know I understand, but it just happened. We are in love, and we want to be together."

"Have you thought about what could happen," said Mammy, "the chances of Sam being caught or worse! What will happen then?"

"God only knows," Kate said, "but I am prepared to make that choice. I will need your help Mam." When they arrived home Kate's Mam shooed the young girl's out to play.

"John," Kate's Mam said addressing her husband who was sitting at the table, "Kate has something to tell you."

"Dad, Sam and I are getting married."

"Oh," said John "is that so and when is all this going to happen?"

"We are getting married when Lent is over," said Kate.

"How come we never heard any of this before?"

"Because" said Kate, trying to be brave, "I am expecting his baby."

My Dad just looked at me. I wished the floor would swallow me up, I turned beet red almost trembling.

"I thought more of that fella," he said. He just reached up to the mantel piece removing his pipe and making a fuss of lighting it. "I am sorry Dad," as I said it, I burst out crying all the tension of the last few days just exploded.

Mam came over and took me in her arms. "There, there! It's not as bad as all that, your dad will come around. We will look after you." Her comfort helped me to calm down. "Come help me with the dinner it will take your mind off it," Mam said.

Having spoken with my family I realised how lucky I was. Although disappointed and feeling upset by my situation my mother, ever the businesswoman, began to plan. "You will get married as soon as you can, I will talk to the priest In Halston St. You will also need a place to live. There is not enough room here, for you a wife and a baby, and I doubt her house would be any different. Anyway, we can see what's available next week or so. There won't be any big celebration just the immediate family. So, don't get any big ideas."

"I am not expecting anything," I answered "but I appreciate your help. I am going to see Kate this afternoon. We will talk and decide what's ahead."

As I walked up to Dominick St I was apprehensive as to the reception I would receive. When I entered the hallway, I met one of the young sisters on the stairs she looked at me and said, "Our Kitty was crying today, you better mind yourself."

Knocking on the door I steeled myself for a difficult encounter, Mrs Glynn answered the door. "Come in Sam." You could feel the tension in the room. Kate's eyes were puffy from crying, but she came towards me and held my hand.

"Kate has been telling us of your problems," said Mrs Glynn "she said that you and she are going to be married?"

It took a couple of seconds for me to reply. "First of all, I have to apologise for bringing any distress to you and your family," I said. "We are in love as I am sure you know, and we can't turn the clock back as to what happened. But I assure you I had planned to marry Kate and look after her for the rest of my life."

"That's all well and good," said Mr Glynn "but you could be in jail or worse tomorrow."

"We know that sir but there is no guarantee for any of us, we just have to do our best."

"How does your mother feel about all this?" asked Mrs Glynn. "She is not thrilled about it but understands the reality of it and has accepted the way it is."

"And we can do no less," said Mrs Glynn. "Off you go the two of ye, we have a lot to talk about," said Mrs Glynn. Kate put on her coat, and we left. When we were out on the street, we both relaxed.

"It wasn't as bad as you expected after all was it?" I asked.

"No, my dad won't speak to me, but Mammy said he will come around."

Chapter 15
The Wedding

Towards the end of March Sean Mac Eoin was captured by crown forces in the train station at Mullingar. He had tried to make a break for it but was intercepted by a patrol and shot through the lung. He was brought to Dublin tied to a stretcher with a gun to his head. Collins had men out to try and rescue him, but he was driven into Dublin by a back road, evading Collins's men and he was taken to Mountjoy Prison, where he was treated in the prison for his injuries. When he recovered he was charged with Treason and eventually sentenced to death. Michael Collins and Mac Eoin were very good friends,

Collins had been best man at his wedding, and he was distressed to think that Sean would be executed. He wanted a plan to try and rescue Mac Eoin. I was now a full-time member of the Squad; our Unit and the ASU were charged with coming up with a plan that would accomplish this.

Emmet Dalton and Paddy Daly, our commander, started drawing up a plan. Emmet Dalton had been a Major in the British Army during the First World War and was now one of our top officers in the ASU. The gist of the plan was we would have to use deception and posing as British soldiers we would get inside the Prison and rescue Mac Eoin. We would need to be convincing and would need a great deal of luck.

We were getting information from some of the prison guards who were sympathetic to our cause as to the lay out of the prison. The front gate was the only way we could get in, there were barricades and machine gun posts positioned guarding the entrance so any kind of frontal attack would be suicide. There was also a big RIC barracks not far away and a cavalry barracks within a mile or so from the prison. So, the only chance of getting in was the pretence of moving the prisoner to another location, posing as British soldiers. we had British uniforms and weapons, we decided if we had British vehicles it be more convincing, the plan required blocking the prison gates from closing an Armoured car was suggested, our first objective was how we would capture an armoured car intact, we were given instructions to observe the movement of the armoured regiment that was stationed there. We would also need transport such as a staff car. The car we could get without too much trouble, the armoured car was another story.

At a special meeting of picked ASU and Squad men we were discussing the problems we faced. Paddy Daly asked, "How many of you lads can drive?"

Only two men were competent drivers. "Ok we will have to have at least 4 or 5 capable of driving and we have to have an experienced driver for the armoured car. Who volunteers for driving?"

I put up my hand along with 6 others. "Good, we start learning tomorrow," said Daly. A few days later 3 of us were sent to Boland's bakery as trainees for their lorries. It was good cover in case anyone asked. I was put with Pat Dolan, an older man who was a regular driver for them, also he was a 1st battalion man. After he made his normal deliveries, we headed up to the Phoenix Park. It was quiet in the park and decent roads with little traffic.

"Ok young fella, this is where you start." I took the driver's seat as he explained the pedals and breaks to me.

"Just take your time and give it a little on the accelerator and let the clutch slowly out that will get us moving." I was excited to learn and managed to get the lorry moving after a stuttering start and a few jumps and bumps.

"Now once you get it moving you have to change the gear for more speed. Press the clutch down and let it out gently and try not to force the stick otherwise it will grind," said Pat. After about an hour or so I had an idea of what I needed to do. "That is as much as we can do today, we don't want anyone asking why we are late. Tomorrow is another day."

When we got back to the yard, we parked the lorry as usual and left. The other lads Jimmy and Frank were waiting when I walked out. "How did you do?" Jimmy asked.

"I didn't crash so ok I think," I answered.

"Yeah it wasn't as hard as I thought," said Frank. "We have to see if we can do it on the street then we will be OK. See you tomorrow."

So, for the next week we continued to learn to drive. My first experience of driving on the city streets was harrowing, my heart was in my mouth for the first while. After we had done my normal starting and stopping in the park it was time to return to the yard. I pulled over to the edge of the road to change with Pat. "Ok lad this time you take us back to the yard and don't get us killed," said Pat.

"Are you sure?" I said. "I am a bit nervous."

"You'll be all right just concentrate and keep your eyes peeled for people running across the road." We set off with me gripping the wheel for dear life. Once we got out on to the road I relaxed, as long as I stayed behind other traffic, I was fine. My only problem occurred when I had to cross the tram lines. Judging speed and distance was something I had to master. By the time I reached the yard I was sweating, but I made it without any major incident. Within a couple of days, I was confident enough to drive around the city.

I had been very busy in the past couple of weeks, what with learning to drive and some extra training for our upcoming mission. Things had settled down with both our families, having got over the initial shock they had gotten used to the idea of our marriage. My mother true to her word had spoken to the priest at Halston Street Church and a tentative date was set for April 18th. I was not looking forward to a conversation with the priest knowing their view on out of wedlock pregnancy. It was now time to introduce Kate to my family. I arranged for Kate to come for dinner on Easter Sunday at our house. I picked up Kate at her house after Mass. Being the anniversary of the 1916 Rising, British troops were on alert with lots of patrols out and about. So, I made it my business to stay out of their way.

Kate was dressed in her finest dress with a lovely hat and looked stunning. It was a bright sunny day and walking along Mary Street gave me a great feeling to have such a beautiful girl on my arm. People from my neighbourhood greeted us as we walked by, it was the first time I had ever walked with a girl and people were curious. Kate had brought some flowers for my Mam, but I could tell she was nervous. "Don't worry, you will be fine," I said.

I knocked on the door Dinah opened the door a big smile on her face. "Welcome," Dinah said. Kate smiled back as she shook hands with Dinah, "come in."

As we entered, we could see Christy and Uncle Jerry were already there. Mam was bending over the fire preparing some of the dinner. I walked over with Kate to Mam. "Mam, this is Kate." Mam stood to greet Kate, she was dressed in black as usual, being a widow, which made her look stern. But she managed a smile as she said, "Welcome to our home Kate, it's nice to finally meet you."

As Kate replied I could feel the tension leaving her. "Thank you for inviting me Mrs Robinson," handing Mam the flowers. With the pleasantries over it was time to meet Christy and Uncle Jerry. They made us feel comfortable and the conversation drifted to asking about Kate's family. We had a lovely dinner, after dinner Ma brought up the subject of our wedding. My mother suggested the 18th of April as the market would be closed that day. Kate did not feel there would be any objection from her family, and that was agreeable with Kate, so we settled on that, as our wedding day.

The day flew by and when we said our goodbyes it was almost 7 o'clock. On our way back to Kates, I asked how she felt. "I feel better now knowing your family. Your mam is very reserved, I am not sure she approves of me."

"It's Ok," I said, "She is like that sometimes; she has been a widow for such a long time she often looks very sad. She will warm up to you."

Both Kate and I were looking forward to being together. It was such a strange time being young in love and caught up in the middle of a war not knowing what lay ahead. We had, through a friend, found a place to live over in Mountjoy Street not too far from where Kate lives. It was just a big room with a fireplace and basic furniture, and I would be able to afford the rent, at least I was getting well paid by the Army. Kate was thrilled knowing she was going to have her own place. The baby was to be born in August.

On the Morning of April 18th, we were all assembled at Halston Street Church, accompanied by our respective families we were going to be married. What an exciting day knowing that from now on Kate and I would be bound together forever. My Mam and all our small family and Uncle Jerry were present. Kate had her Mam, Dad, and older sister Sarah there. Our friends Bill Kiernan and Maggie Burke were our witnesses. Marrying a woman who was with child, although common in these troubled times, was not condoned by the church, however the attending priest was very understanding and dealt with the situation with dignity.

Looking at Kate and taking the solemn vows of marriage is something I will never forget. Leaving the church as a husband and a potential father I felt a profound responsibility to do my very best.

My mother had made arranged for a wedding breakfast at the nearby Ormond Hotel. Although there was an undercurrent of tension, the families not knowing one another, my mother and Mrs Glynn got on well and we all enjoyed a smashing breakfast. Christy raised a glass and welcomed Kate into the family.

After the breakfast we left with Maggie and Bill and walked to our new flat on Mountjoy Street. A few of the neighbours recognised us as newlyweds and wished us well. On reaching our flat Maggie and Bill said their goodbyes and left. We went up the stairs, took the key and opened the door I lifted Kate and carried her across the threshold and entered our new home. It was all we could hope for to live a long and happy life together.

Chapter 16
Armoured Car

I was still involved with watching movement of military personnel and keeping my driving up to scratch. Any time a driver was needed I volunteered. On one occasion I got to drive a touring car all the way to Greystones where Eamonn De Valera was staying bringing Mick Collins, Cathal Brugha and Paddy Daly to a meeting. From that meeting it was to be decided to mount a large-scale operation in which the Custom House on the Quays would be attacked and burned.

Things had moved on and some reconnaissance had noticed a pattern of an armoured car waiting at the intersection at the cattle market on North Circular Road. Every week, the British forces picked up cattle for slaughter for their own use and then shipped the beef to different barracks. They loaded the cattle on lorry and took them to be slaughtered. The HQ for the armoured car was in Marlborough Barracks which was only a short distance from the cattle market.

Because they did it so often their routine was a bit slack and it wasn't unknown for the soldiers to skip into the pub on the corner to grab a quick pint, pretending to use the toilet. The officer in charge was usually a young lieutenant, he would have a sergeant, a driver and a couple of guards. The officer usually travelled in the lorry. The lorry often left first, leaving the armoured car to follow. Sometimes the Sergeant and one of the soldiers entered the pub and had a quick pint or two. This only left the driver with the car. So, planning began to see if it was possible to capture the armoured car. Paddy Daly put the plan forward and we came up with a way of putting it into effect.

We needed transport, a hiding place for the armoured car and British uniforms. These were all arranged, and we began to shadow the small convoy. I was going to be Emmet Dalton's driver. He would be dressed in his old Major's uniform; he would have Joe Leonard dressed as a lieutenant with him. Our sergeant with us in the car, a former British soldier Pat Mac Crea, was familiar with driving armoured cars. Our uniforms would have the insignia of Military police. We would also have six of our Squad men, four in the pub and two scouting outside for trouble. If the NCO and soldier went into the pub, the Major would confront the driver and berate him for the lack of security. In the meantime, our men in the pub would deal with the soldiers in there. Then we would commandeer the armoured car. In theory it was as sound a plan as we could come up with, however we would need some luck as well.

We watched the first time, there was no opportunity to execute our plan. The personnel had changed, the officer in charge was more experienced and the detail all left at the same time. The next time it was the younger officer in charge, so they rotated each time. We were parked up a laneway away from the cattle market. Our scouts were watching as soon as the lorry left. The sergeant and his comrade made a bee line for the pub.

The barman knew the sergeant by sight and our men had a chat with him. He was cooperative and was a sympathiser with the cause. He was to engage the soldiers in conversation while our men would hold them up and disarm them. The bar man greeted the sergeant, "What will it be Sergeant?" asked the barman.

"Two pints," answered the sergeant leaning his rifle against the counter.

"A cold auld day out there," said an old man at the bar making conversation.

"It is that," said the sergeant.

The old man said, "It reminds me of my days in the trenches at Mons, we needed a drop of poteen to still the cold."

"Sounds good," said the sergeant.

"Would you like to try some," said the barman, "on the house?" Looking around the sergeant saw no one paying any attention to them.

"Ok we'll try it." The barman poured from a bottle under the counter, a clear liquid, a generous portion for each of them. "Slainte," said the old man and they each took a big gulp. The fiery liquid almost took their breath away and soon the atmosphere was pleasant, the barman and the old man kept up a conversation which distracted the soldiers.

We drove the car into the market and came to a sharp stop behind the armoured car. The Private was leaning against the car smoking. As I braked the soldier looked up startled, Dalton jumped out of the car. "What's going on here?" he shouted, the soldier sprung to attention.

"Nothing, Sir," answered the private. "I can see that! What is your name Private?" The soldier had just noticed the Military Police insignia.

"Private Marsden T. 7597684," answered the soldier.

"Where's the rest of the detail?" asked the Major. "They went to the toilet across the road, Sir."

"Well we will see about that," said Dalton. The Lieutenant walked up to the soldier, a drawn revolver in his hand. "If you want to see the rest of the day don't open your mouth or I will shoot you dead," he said. The soldier almost collapsed with fright. Taking his weapon and opening the armoured car door the Lieutenant motioned him into the car. Our driver and the lieutenant got in with him, once inside they handcuffed the soldier and blindfolded him. Our man started the armoured car and started to drive away. The sergeant hearing the roar of the car starting up ran to the window. "For fuck's sake, what is that fool trying to do driving that car?"

With that our men in the pub surrounded them removing their weapons and tying their hands behind them. They were completely taken by surprise and offered no resistance. There was a van at the back of the pub, they were bundled into it and driven out into the country where they were released that night not knowing where they were. It would take a while for them to get back. They would not be in any hurry more than likely facing a court martial.

We got the armoured car to a safe hiding place down by the docks. There was a disused warehouse we could hide it in till needed. The soldier in the armoured car was put in the car with us and also driven out into the mountains where we let him go. It would take ages for him to get back. The military were taken by surprise with the loss of such a powerful weapon. Detectives and military descended on the pub to question the barman and customers. They found the barman had disappeared along with the customers. No one was giving them any information. It was now Wednesday, we had to hide the armoured until Sunday May 13th which was the day scheduled for the escape attempt.

The morning came and we were going to make the attempt the rescue. Pat McCrae and another squad member were in the armoured car. Emmet Dalton and Joe Leonard were in the touring car with me driving and Jim Sullivan beside me. Dalton had a fake order to take custody of Mac Eoin. They also had some duplicate keys to the prison supplied by Collins' agents. When Dalton showed the guard at the gate his orders the gate was opened. There was also an inner gate McCrae was to drive in and the prisoner would be put in the armoured car while our car waited outside.

Dalton and Leonard entered the prison and headed straight to the Head Warder's office. They demanded Mac Eoin be brought down. In the meantime, McCrae was pretending to turn the armoured car around and manoeuvred the car so the gates could not be closed. There were also two women at the gate arguing with the warder about delivering parcels to one of the prisoners. The Warder was having a bad day and started to close the gate. We jumped out of the car with pistols drawn to threaten the Warder. One of the guards noticed the pistols and opened fire. A bullet creased my shoulder and we returned fire.

Then a machine gun opened splattering against the gate and the armoured car. McCrae couldn't swivel the turret gun to engage so we started firing from the cover of the Armoured car. In the meantime the Head Warder had grown suspicious, so Dalton and Leonard had to make a run for it. They came out with pistols drawn and began firing as they ran for their lives. The bullets were tearing holes in the wooden gate and reverberating off the steel in the armoured car creating an awful racket. McCrae had already started the car and had it moving, as Dalton and Leonard raced through the gate they Jumped into the Armoured car, we piled into the touring car behind them and sped away.

The Plan was McCrea would take the Armoured car into a wooded area near Finglas ,dismantle the weapons Take what we could and dump the car. Another van would be there to pick him up .The road was quiet and we were able to get down to Smithfield quickly and dumped the car in the distillery yard we had used on occasion. We left the car and changed into civies and dispersed. We had been very lucky. I had a slight wound on my shoulder and everyone else was Ok. I went up to a doctor's office I knew in Capel St He dressed the wound. It wasn't serious and wouldn't cause me any trouble, it would just be a bit sore for a little while.

When I got back to our house Kate was shocked to see me injured. I had to reassure her I was ok. The authorities were stunned by the audacity of our attempt. The British even had an aeroplane up looking for the armoured car. Collins was disappointed by our failure to rescue Mac Eoin but the publicity of our escapade made up for it.

Chapter 17
The Custom House Battle

The planning for our attack on the Custom House had progressed and a huge amount of work and organising was needed. Combustible materials had to be accumulated, transport had to be provided to carry the vast amount of materiel required including the tins needed. Paraffin oil was the best to use and the safest one to use Petrol tended to explode and was less suitable. The ASU augmented by several battalions of the Dublin Brigade and the Squad would be used on the operation. It would involve more than 130 men. This would be the biggest operation yet tried.

Engineers would be responsible to disable telephone communication while 1st and 2nd battalion men would fire the building. The Squad were tasked with security and guarding prisoners. Other units would be deployed to hinder the Fire Department from responding; we also had great cooperation from some members of the Fire Department. ASU men would create a perimeter around to cover the men inside. It was complex plan that required split second timing and a good deal of luck. Our orders were to be assembled at different points and be ready to go at 12.30pm on May 25th. We would arrive, just as the employees would be getting ready for their lunch. Therefore, we should be able to blend in with the workers.

Wednesday May 25th, 1921, dawned a bright day with a hint of summer in the air. I rose early as usual Kate was up and getting ready to go to work in Jacobs. It was now obvious that she was expecting a child, the baby due in early August. She would only be able to work for few weeks more. We sat and had tea and toast together making plans for Sunday when we were to go to the Glynn's house for dinner our first time as a married couple. We had been married almost five weeks and loved being together.

My arm was now healed, and I was feeling good. I dressed as usual in a suit and tie as if I was a clerk working in the city. Kate was first to leave; she would catch a tram that would take her within a short walk to Jacobs. I gave her a hug and kissed her forehead saying I would see her at teatime. I watched as she crossed the street making for the tram stop. I hadn't told her about the action we were going to perpetrate today.

The Squad met at our meeting place at 34 Lower Gardiner St We would be working with all the different units involved. Tom Ennis of the Squad was the officer commanding the operation. We drew our weapons; I had a Mauser automatic with 3 spare magazines. The Squad would mainly be employed to hold the staff and any police captive and deal with any soldiers we might encounter until we had the building on fire. Then we would release the civilians and mixing with the workers in order to escape. All the different units had their own assignments. The whole plan depended on everyone working in concert.

We were not used to operating with so many people at the same time and there had not been any way to train for this. Also, for a large number of the battalion men this would be their first time in action. But these were brave men committed to carrying out their orders.

All units were to move off at 12.30pm which would put us in the Custom House around 12.45 pm that would blend in with lots of workers and staff moving around going to lunch. The whole operation was supposed to take only 25 to 30 minutes. Tom Keogh and myself walked from Gardiner Street down towards the Custom House. Other groups of men approached from different directions, no one seemed to be taking any particular notice of us. Store Street police station was within sight of our target but so far there was no unusual activity there.

As we came abreast of the entrance opposite Beresford Place, we quickly made our way inside. There was an urgency about the place as volunteers started bringing in combustible materials and tins of petrol and paraffin from a lorry parked at the road. There was a stream of men carrying in what that needed, some men also had sledgehammers and crow bars to break up any wood. Our men were making their way to the top floor where most of the structure was made with timber, offices desks and partitions. They evacuated the staff sending them down the stairs under guard and began to break up any wooden structures. All paper, books or ledgers were piled up in the middle of the floor, doused with paraffin or petrol and set alight. The women and clerks immediately left some of the supervisors had to be persuaded to leave.

Once down the stairs we collected them together in the centre of the building. Staff were flabbergasted to see armed men in the building, they couldn't believe what was happening. We had not been in the building long, about 10 minutes, when we heard shots from outside. I was covering a group of people, including one of the guards. Tom went to the window and looked out, there was a Crossley tender and Auxiliary troopers were fanning out and taking up firing positions. Then we heard an explosion from the Abbey Street side, it sounded like our men had thrown grenades and were engaging another Crossley tender full of Tans.

Windows in the building were being hit with bullets ricocheting off granite walls. We went to the windows and started to return fire. Most of the weapons issued to the volunteers were small calibre revolvers and held only 4 to 6 rounds. We would not be very effective from a range of more than 50 yards. No sooner had the battle began when a Lancia armoured car arrived on the scene and started strafing the building while driving up and down the street.

The situation was quickly becoming grave. Our prisoners were starting to panic, especially the women, as the smoke began to form black clouds in the building combined with the roar of the flames as the fire took hold. British army soldiers arrived outside and began to advance towards us. We were now completely surrounded. I couldn't believe things had deteriorated so quickly. There was a machine gun now covering our main way out. One of our men of the Squad, Sean Doyle, was killed trying to escape though that entrance.

He was mowed down by machine gun fire, the machine gun chewed lumps off the granite walls and caused several injuries to both our men and some of the staff. The upper floors were now an inferno, we could hear windows bursting from the heat. The roar of the flame escaping through the dome was frightening. Auxiliaries had now gained entrance into the building but retired when seeing the state of the fire. Every side of the building was now under fire from the troops outside. We were supposed to retire when we heard three whistle blasts which would be the signal to get out.

The noise was such that we couldn't hear anything but the noise of the battle. Our only choice was to shepherd the civilians out with their hands up and mix with them and hope in the confusion try to escape. We had only been in the building less than 25 minutes.

Someone made a crude white flag and waved it out the entrance door. The firing on the entrance stopped with army moving up to cover the door. The troops outside were shouting, "Come out with your hands up." We started to move the civilians forward towards the exit. We had to dump our arms and mix with the crowd. The women were now crying, and some were helping others who had suffered a variety of injuries in the ensuing panic. I had my hands up; we as were all herded together and surrounded by military and Tans and shepherded away from the burning building.

The men were separated from the women; Officers watched and tried to sort us all out. Several of the senior employees had managed to get out and were now identifying their own people. Standing in line we were being asked who we were as they tried to weed us out. When the information given was not what was expected beatings were common. The soldiers were in foul mood. The fire was now raging out of control and there was very little evidence of the Fire Brigade who had been detained by ASU units tasked with that job. When my turn came, I had an army officer and a tan to contend with. "What's your name?"

"Jeremiah Robinson," I answered.

"I was here on an errand for my boss," I said, "I have a letter from him in my pocket." With that I started to move my hand to get the letter. The Tan almost stuck his bayonet in my face. I stopped with the bayonet an inch from my eye. As the officer pulled my coat open and searched me and he found the letter but was not impressed and threw it away. "The only letter you're going to need is one from the hang man," he said laughing and moving to the next man.

I thought I was going to lose my eye, the hatred on the Tans face was frightening, the bayonet still an inch from my face.

Looking around while standing I could see the building engulfed and the fire completely out of control. Some firemen had finally arrived but there wasn't much they could do; their hoses mainly damping down the granite walls giving off steam in some instances. There were groups of us lined up in different areas depending on which exit we were able to get out. By this time, a large force of military had arrived with more armoured cars and lorries.

Crowds had gathered on the other side of the Liffey watching the building burn. We were kept under heavy guard with no chance of slipping away. I was surprised by the number of men under guard. There were bodies lying outside the building where they had died, it was a sad sight. We had been standing for a long time; every so often officers would go up and down the line questioning and searching us. Then they started loading us into lorries again under heavy guard, they were taking no chances soldiers with fixed bayonet's lined the street.

As we were loaded into the lorries, I could see some of our men that I knew. We did not speak to one another in case it would give us away. They had four lorries jammed with men and armoured cars ahead and behind as we left the Custom House. The convoy moved at speed to discourage anyone trying to escape. We were brought to Arbor Hill Barracks where we discharged from the lorries. Herded into a common area again surrounded by soldiers we were again lined up for inspection. This went on for some time a few of the lads were out on their feet, some with minor injuries and burns. The officers finally let us sit down. We again were separated into groups then they brought in water and bread, and we were allowed to have a drink and some bread.

Some medics attended to the more seriously injured men dressing wounds. I was surprised at how many of us had been captured, the men captured represented a large part of both Squad and ASU, our most experienced fighters.

We sat whispering to each other trying to find out what had happened. It was hard to glean any information other than the fact the Custom House had been completely destroyed which had been our primary objective. We had taken casualties, but no one knew to what extent. Looking back, anyone on the inside was trapped as soon as the soldiers arrived. And even though we had more men than usual we were lightly armed; revolvers are no match for armoured cars with Hotchkiss machine guns. Plus, the confusion with civilian prisoners and a raging fire made it difficult to mount any kind of counterattack our weapons were only good for street fighting at short range.

So, it was inevitable we would have to surrender. Sitting on the floor I felt dejected not knowing what lay ahead wondering if Kate knew about the attack. I am sure Christy would let her know as soon as he could. Christy had been with the men holding up the fire brigade.

After a couple of hours, just as darkness fell, we were roused by the guards again. In small groups we were moved out into the yard and loaded again on lorries, there was about twenty of us jammed into the back of the lorry. We left Arbor Hill and headed across the Liffey towards Kilmainham. When we arrived at Kilmainham it was now dark the gate opened, and we drove inside. It was like some medieval scene. Guards were lined up in two rows with fixed bayonets from the lorry to the entrance of the jail.

Torches were lighted, fixed to the walls casting shadows across the yard. We were ordered down from the lorry and again lined up and we would have to pass through this cauldron of venom and hate to reach the door. The ones in front were hesitant but were forced forward. As we started to run towards the door we were hit with rifles and batons, we were spat upon and called all kinds of names. Although we were not badly injured running the gauntlet it was a humiliating and frightening, an incident I will never forget.

Once inside the shock of being in such a terrible place hit us. The place was so cold and forbidding, two hundred years of Irish suffering embedded in the stone floors we walked on. The guards separated us again and marched us up through the prison. We went deeper into the depths of the prison, the place lit with candles the grey walls stained with dampness till eventually came to an opening to a cell with a metal door.

"Ok, inside," ordered the guard. I looked in, it looked like a cave barely six feet wide, about ten feet long. A bucket in the corner and a kind of board on the floor to sleep on. I felt so low as I entered prison and wondered if ever, I would see daylight again. Then the metal door slammed shut and a metal bar slid home leaving me completely isolated lonely and dejected.

Chapter 18
Captured

Kate was at work when she began to hear whispers of an attack in the city. At lunch time she went outside and from the street a huge black cloud was visible. Military vehicles were racing down to the city centre loaded with troops. A feeling of dread came over her. One of the carters was coming back into the factory, Kate called to him. "Do you know what's going on?," she asked. The man answered, "There's been a big attack at the Custom House, the place is on fire. There was a lot of fighting, some people were killed, a whole lot captured."

"Oh my God! Oh my God I hope he is all right."

"What's the matter Kate," asked her friend Joan.

"There was a big attack on the Custom House. I don't know if Sam is all right, Listen I'll have to go and see what I can find out," Kate said.

"Will you tell Mr Gibbons I had to leave; tell him I wasn't well." With that she started walking as quickly as she could towards Sam's mothers' house. It was hard to walk fast being six months pregnant. By the time she got there she was out of breath and exhausted. When she knocked on the door Mrs Robinson answered. One look at Kate, and she knew something was wrong. "Come in what's wrong? Sit down, Kate."

"The IRA attacked the Custom House today, there was a lot of men captured and some killed. I don't know where Sam is," Kate said, "I was hoping Christy could tell me where is?"

"Oh, Sacred heart of God. Christy left here this morning in his brown suit; I hope they are both alright. I will ask Mr McGuire to find out what he can," Said Mrs Robinson. "You stay here till we find out." After we had some tea, we went outside the sky was still lit up by the fire. Mr McGuire came back he didn't have any real news other than a lot of prisoners were taken. The evening dragged on. After it got dark, we heard someone at the front door.

Christy came in he looked pale and distressed. "Thank God your home, do you know where Sam is?" Mrs Robinson asked.

Seeing me sitting there Christy came over, "Kate," he said, "Sam has been captured with a whole lot of other men. They took them to Arbor Hill that's all we know so far. It will be tomorrow before we can get any more information. One of our lads saw Sam taken in one of the lorries."

Kate started to cry. Dinah put her arms around her trying to comfort her. "Dinah, Kate will stay here for now. Christy, you go over to Aunt Mary's. We will look after Kate," said Mrs Robinson. Kate walked to the bedroom and lay on the bed, her thoughts only of Sam wondering how he was. Her whole world had been turned upside down in a few short hours. It would be a couple of days before they got proper information about Sam's whereabouts.

Meanwhile as Sam woke from a fitful sleep it was still very dark. There was no ambient light to see around the cell. When dawn broke later, he could see a small, barred window high up on the wall. The cell was small about 10 feet long and six feet wide. The walls were damp and grey a breeze was flowing through the barred window. He was able to jump up and catch the bars and haul himself up in order to look out. There was no way to see other than holding on to the bars for a little while. All I could make out were some houses about fifty yards from the prison. Knowing the location of the Jail I figured out I was in the back part facing east. I felt humiliated by the fact I had been captured.

I was cold, the dampness had penetrated my bones. Alone in my cell I knew I would have to steel myself to the situation and conditions I found myself in. I would have to learn to cope with prison, I was young, tough and fit. So, I just had to accept that I had to adapt to being a prisoner. I knew I was not alone as several ASU men had been taken along with me and were also brought to Kilmainham. I thought we would have been put together in cells and I was surprised to be isolated. But then it is easier to break someone's spirit if they are on their own. I will have to adjust to the routine of prison life.

After a while I heard the cover over the spy hole in the door open, I just sat on the board on the floor and watched, whoever it was outside said nothing and slammed the cover shut. I listened trying to hear anyone talking but could only make out sounds of movement in the corridor. I stood up and started to do some exercises to warm up. Then the door was opened, and a guard shouted me to 'slop out.' It took me a minute to understand what he wanted.

"Empty the piss bucket," he said. I picked up the bucket and emptied it into a larger one on wheels pushed by another prisoner. A little while later another prisoner came around with breakfast. He had a big bucket of porridge, tea and bread. I was given a tin plate and cup with a spoon. The tea was at least hot, the porridge filled a gap, and I enjoyed the bread.

After breakfast we were all brought down to the yard with guards and lined up for inspection. We were not allowed to talk. There were six of us from our block I recognised Jim Sullivan from the ASU, the others I did not know Two officers came and started asking us our names, checking the names against a list they had. I gave my name as Jeremiah Robinson which did not make an impression on them, we were then allowed to walk around the yard. We couldn't talk as we were separated from each other. Once the half hour was up, we were returned to our cells. The six of us were on the same corridor.

I was about halfway along. The walls and the door were very thick, and it was very difficult to hear anyone unless the spy hole was open. The day went by slowly I couldn't help but wonder whether Kate knew if I was alright. I was worried about her especially with her expecting our baby. I remembered what happened to Annie, her cousin, worrying about her Tommy.

Kate was still staying at the Robinsons as she wanted to be where Christy was, he was her only hope of getting any information. It was very hard not knowing if Sam was ok, being six months pregnant she worried if her unborn child would ever get to meet its father. After about a week Christy had got word of Sam. Information had come through the grapevine regarding the men captured and Sam's name was included. Now they had to wait to see what arrangements might be made in order to visit him.

Being incarcerated in Kilmainham was different than Mountjoy as there were all kinds of prisoners in Mountjoy whereas Kilmainham held only political prisoners. Also, Mountjoy was a fairly new prison, and Kilmainham was very old, some areas of the prison almost derelict. Mrs Robinson said she would make inquiries about visiting Sam, she suggested Kate not go back to work as it might be too stressful with all that was going on. "Kate if you want you can stay here till we know what is happening," Mrs Robinson said.

"Thanks Mrs Robinson, but we just got used to our own place and I would like to stay there. My sister Maggie said she would stay with me."

"That's good, you need someone with you. We will be here if you need anything. You shouldn't be on your own. By the way you should call me Lizzy, after all you are family."

"Thanks again Lizzy. I will be back tomorrow; I have to go over to my Mam's today."

Kate made her way over to Dominick St Thank goodness her Mam lived on the first landing. Her Mam was doing some washing as she came in. "Kate! Are you Ok?"

"Yes, Mammy, I am OK."

"Did you find out anything about Sam?" her mam asked. "Yes, he is in Kilmainham, there's a whole lot of them there, his brother Christy got word from some of the men."

"Well at least we know he is alright, sit down I'll make you some to eat in a minute, your Da should be home soon."

"Sam's mammy is trying to find out if we can go and visit him, but it may take a while to sort out. I hope it doesn't take too long," Kate said.

"There's nothing you can do you just have to look after yourself for now," Kate's mother said.

The month of June brought better weather and I had adjusted to prison life. The days were long and monotonous, some of the lads were trying to communicate with one another, notes were being passed during our exercise in the yard. We learned that there was talk of a truce happening. Then as we walked around the yard I got pulled out by the guard. I was marched into a room near the guard house, I thought I was in for a hiding. Once inside I was stood up against the wall two officers came in.

"What is your name?" They asked again. I gave my name, Jeremiah Robinson. They checked their lists again conferring with each other. Then one of them walked to the door and called out for some soldiers to come in. Three soldiers came into the room I thought this is it there going to do me. The soldiers lined up on the other side of the room. The officers told them to take their time. As they looked at me, I realised I recognised one of them.

I tried to be calm, but my heart was racing, the one I knew was had been one of the detail with the armoured car we stole. His eyes bored into me, and he said pointing at me, "That's one of the men that hijacked our armoured car," he said.

The officers glowered at me. "That's you fucked lad," the older one said. He walked over standing right in front of me smiling trying to intimidate me. I just looked straight ahead expecting any minute I would get a kicking.

"Take this bastard back to his cell," he ordered the guard, "The hangman will have him!"

As I was taken back to my cell, my mind was racing. I had been officially recognised now. Needless to say, I was worried, if my name was now put on the 'known' list I could be tried and executed. There was nothing I could do only wait and see what happens.

Chapter 19
Kilmainham

Time dragged on as we got used to the prison routine the conditions were just about bearable. At least it was June and not winter. The worst part was no communication between the prisoners and no word from my family. I would turn up the bucket in my cell and could jump up and catch the bars I started shouting through the window, depending on the conditions outside we tried to talk to each other. Sometimes you would hear someone singing, the bars were far away from you as the walls were so thick you would have to lever yourself up onto the sill to see out. At least we managed to get some information from one another I learned the men on either side of me were from the 4th battalion.

There was still a rumour going around about a truce. It was now the middle of June, and I celebrated my 17th birthday in prison. Over three weeks had passed and still no word from home. One day while I was looking out the window some people had gathered on the bridge just outside the prison and were waving and shouting up to the prison trying to contact some of the prisoners. I watched and listened as much as possible. After a short time, they seemed to have made progress and were talking with one of the prisoners.

This gave us hope of getting information out as we could not speak to each other in the yard. This way we could tell them who was in here. Once it started it became our lifeline to our families. Word travelled and soon everyday there were visitors on the bridge. The location of my cell made it difficult because of the angle from the bridge but we would try to get word along from cell to cell and down to the people outside. We would ask the visitors to the bridge to contact our families. Only the cells on the top of the east wing could see over the prison wall.

It took a little while, but Christy found out about the people contacting the prisoners from the bridge. Christy made his way up to Kilmainham. Across the road from the prison was the HQ of the British Army in Ireland in the Old Royal Hospital built for Veterans of the wars in India and Africa. Needless to say, he was cautious in his approach as the DMP had started watching the people on the bridge. He began surveillance and discovered the back gardens of some of the houses afforded a better location for communication. He approached one of the houses and knocked on the door. A woman came to the door, "Yes what do you want?" She asked.

"I was wondering if I could go into your back garden I want to try talking to my brother in the prison."

"Go off outta that, I don't want people traipsing through my house," she said as she started to close the door. I'd make it worth your while! Christy said taking a ten-shilling note from his pocket. She stopped mid-way and looked at the money.

"Well," she said, reaching for the money, "maybe it would be ok for a little while."

Pocketing the money, she made her way to the back yard with Christy following. The back garden had a raised area at the back, so Christy made for that area.

Christy watched as he could hear some of the conversations going on with the inmates and their families, when there was a lull he shouted as loud as he could, "Sam Robinson." There was no reply, he tried again "Saaammm can you hear me?"

Sam was sitting down and thought he heard something, he pulled himself up on to the sill. He looked in the direction of the bridge. There were some people still calling up to the prison Then out of the corner of his eye he caught sight of someone in a garden. Looking down he saw Christy he started to wave at Christy and shouted his name. "Christy! It's me can you hear me?"

When Christy looked up and caught sight of Sam he was delighted. "Sam are you OK?" He shouted back. "I'm Ok brother especially after seeing you."

Sam's mind was reeling filled with thoughts of what he should ask. The joy of seeing his brother almost overwhelmed Christy he tried to keep it together. Shouting your messages across the divide was not ideal. "How is Kate doing is she all right?" Sam shouted, "Is the baby ok?"

Christy replied, "She's doing great, her sister is staying with her. The woman in this house let me in to talk to you. I will ask her if Mam and Kate can come to see you."

"Yeah, that would be great!" Sam said, "do you need anything? I will see if we can get a parcel to you."

"Put the keys to the front door in the parcel."

"Anyway, Sam thank God you're Ok. It's great to see you." You couldn't really have a proper conversation under the circumstances but the relief of knowing Sam was all right was all that mattered. "I will be back in a couple of days mind yourself till I come back."

"Thanks Christy," Sam said as he watched Christy walk away. His spirits soared knowing about Kate. As Christy went into the house the woman was in her kitchen. "Well, I see you got to talk to someone," she said.

"Listen," Christy said, "if my Mam wanted to come up would that be all right?"

The woman hesitated before answering. "If the arrangement is the same, I am sure I think it could work for both of us," the woman said. "I could do with a few bob!"

Christy looked at her and nodded, not showing his disgust with this woman. "I'll be in touch", he said and left. Sam was so happy having been able to talk to his family after such a long time. He was not alone anymore.

Christy hurried to his mother's house knowing he was carrying good news. Lizzy and Dinah would be home at this time as the market normally finished around lunch time. When he arrived as usual, they were having their dinner after a long day out, immediately Lizzy could see that Christy was excited. "Great news," he said, "I got to talk to Sam today."

"Oh, thank God," both the women exclaimed blessing themselves.

"My prayers are answered," said Lizzy. "Tell me, how did you manage that?" Lizzy asked. Christy went on to explain about approaching the woman in the house behind the prison and paying her for letting him in. "Her name is Bridie Redmond."

"Well, it takes all kinds to make a world but at least we know he is OK," said Lizzy. "You have to go up to see Kate right away and let her know, she'll be over the moon. Tell her we will all pay a visit as soon as we can arrange it. So how was Sam?" His mam asked.

"I could only see him from a distance, but he sounded good especially when he knew it was me. It's very hard to talk when you have to keep shouting to be heard. They keep all the men in separate cells I can only imagine what kind of place it is. It's bad enough outside. Anyway, I'm going up to see Kate right away give her the good news."

Christy made his way to Mountjoy Street when he arrived, he got no answer. One of the neighbours saw him, "Kate is down at her mother's place."

"Thanks, I'll head on down there. It is not far over to Dominick St." He went up and knocked on the flat door. Maggie answered, he asked for Kate. When Kate came out as soon as she saw Christy, she feared the worst, "Is everything all right?" She asked.

Seeing the colour drain from her face Christy hastened to tell her, "Great news, I saw Sam today! It took a couple of seconds for Kate to understand Christy. You actually saw him?!" She asked.

"Yes, I did, he is OK." With that Kate threw her arms around Christy hugging him at the same time calling her Mam. The door opened and her Mam took in the scene realizing who was at the door. "Come in Christy, what are you doing out here?"

"Hello Mrs Glynn, I just came over with some good news for Kate." Ushering Christy in, at the same time taking Kates's arm seeing how pale she was. "Now let's all sit down, and we can talk properly. Maggie make us a cup of tea,"

Maggie busied herself while Kate asked again, "Did you say you saw Sam?"

"Yes, I went to the prison and people were making contact with some of the prisoners shouting up from the bridge. I managed to get into a garden behind the prison where we knew most of our lads were being kept. I started calling out his name and sure enough he answered me. We started talking and he is in good shape. I am going to make arrangements for us to go back there and talk to Sam." Christy told them. "Can you believe it Mammy? Sam is Ok."

"Oh, thank God I was worried sick he was hurt or worse?" Kate said. Holding her stomach now seven months pregnant, she felt the baby move. "The baby is excited too," she announced. They all had a good laugh and the tension of the last few weeks just drifted away. Everything is going to be all right.

Chapter 20
Messages

It was another week before Christy approached Bridie Redmond with a request to speak to Sam. "My mother and his wife would like to talk to my brother. Can I bring them by?" asked Christy.

"When do they want to come?" Bridie answered. "Is this afternoon Ok?,"

"Yes, I will be here, the same arrangement?"

"No problem," said Christy, with that he went off to tell his mother. Both Kate and Lizzy were anxious to see Sam and were waiting ready to go when Christy arrived. They took a tram that went to Inchicore which left them not far from the Gaol. When they got to the Redmond house Bridie was in the front yard. Seeing people arriving she stopped what she was doing and walked over.

Christy said, "This my Ma and my brother's wife we would like to go into your back yard ok?" Bridie opened the front door and led them through to the backyard. Christy handed her another 10-shilling note which disappeared in a flash. When they got into the yard Christy made a loud whistle and started calling to Sam. On hearing the commotion outside Sam jumped up and pulled himself onto the ledge looking out through the bars of the window. He could not believe his eyes, in the garden was Kate, his mother and Christy all waving and shouting his name.

Putting his arm out through the bars he began to wave back. It was hard to see their features at such a distance but there was no mistaking who was there. He was overcome with emotion and began to shout with joy. Kate was overwhelmed seeing Sam for the first time in over a month, tears rolled down her cheeks as she waved enthusiastically unable to speak. Lizzy called to Sam asking if he was ok. There was some stilted conversation, it was difficult to speak other than shouting, so just standing seeing Sam was enough to bring comfort to the women.

After a little while it was time to leave saying goodbye the women started back to the house. Christy shouted to Sam they would return next week. Christy arranged with Bridie that they would return the following week. The small party walked to the bridge each with their own thoughts, drained by the experience especially the women they hailed a passing hackney for the journey home. Sam couldn't believe he had seen his family it was up lifting, and his spirit soared he would get through this no matter what.

The thoughts of being in touch with my family and knowing I was with my comrades made prison life more bearable. I made a conscious effort to stay fit doing more exercise in my cell. I began a routine of physical and mental exercise to make me stronger. The weeks passed quickly, then in early July we learned that a Truce had been arranged between British and the IRA. Suddenly everything in the prison changed. The doors to our cells were thrown open and we were allowed to mix and talk with fellow prisoners.

I needn't tell you we were so excited to be able to communicate with each other. I learned about what had happened at the Custom House that day. We had had five casualties that day and eighty of us captured. This was hard to take as we did not have huge numbers to begin with, the only consolation was that our objective had been achieved. The burning of the Custom House had accelerated the talks and so a truce had now been achieved.

Our new freedom within the prison was welcome. We were allowed to move around the gaol and began to meet members of our own units. Quite a number of ASU and Squad men had been captured and once allowed to congregate information was shared and families informed. Once again, a chain of command was established. We had no idea how long the Truce talks would go on and had to be prepared for the worst.

Once the restrictions had been lifted, we were informed we would allowed have letters and parcels from our families. There were no female visitors allowed into Kilmainham, only in extreme circumstances. So, we would only have the visits from our families from outside the prison. These visits had a different tone now as families looked forward to seeing us freed as soon as an agreement would be reached. The week after the talks were announced I heard my name being called, one of my cell mates was calling my name.

"Sam where are you? Your brother is outside calling for you." I went back to my own cell and climbed up on the ledge. Sure, enough Christy was in the garden behind the Gaol. I waved out and called to him, "Christy." Christy looked up and waved to me. "Where's Mam and Kate?," I shouted.

"Sam, Kate had her baby last night!"

I was stunned for a moment. "Did you say Kate had our baby?" I shouted back.

"Yes," he replied, "a little girl."

It took another few seconds to sink in. "My God a little baby girl. That's fantastic, is Kate all right?" I asked.

"She is with her Mam and is being well looked after," Christy told me. "The baby is a few weeks early, but she is lovely and healthy" Christy said.

I was a dad! I couldn't believe it. How things had changed. "I have to go now, I will be back in a couple of days," Christy said.

"Thanks Christy. That's great news." As I climbed down from the sill I wondered, all the what ifs came into my mind but for now I would be positive. I had a wife and a baby; I had my own little family.

I received my first parcel at the end of July it was very welcome. A change of clothes and some small packages of biscuits and a cake, but most of all there was a letter from Kate and my mother. These were precious as I could read these over and over whenever I needed to. Kate told me of the heartache she felt seeing me in the prison, and how she was managing. Fortunately, she had been at her mother's house when the baby started to come.

She told me, "I went to Mammy's house with Maggie, we were going for our tea. After tea I started to feel pains and I thought I was imagining things, but Mammy knew that labour pains had started. She went for Nellie Dillon; she was experienced delivering babies. Nellie Dillon sent all the children and Dad out to the neighbours, and they started preparing for delivering the baby. I thought I was going to die; the pains were terrible I thought I would die, and it took a lot longer than I expected. But in the end, we have a beautiful little girl. She has a mop of black hair and a dark complexion just like you she is gorgeous. You will love her! I am sending you a picture I got taken at Jerome's in Henry St so you can see her, she is a month old already. It must be hard for you locked up but at least there are talks and people are saying there might be peace after all. I miss you and can't wait for you to come home to us."

Chapter 21
Release

Time dragged on in Kilmainham, it was now well into August. Talks were still going on, but at least conditions in the Gaol were relaxed and we were allowed to mix together. Some lads were learning to speak Irish, others had started a dramatic group and were going to put on a play. Our biggest problem was physical exercise. The prison had no real area for football, but it did have walls and among the prisoners were lads that played handball. And so, a handball tournament was organised. The excitement created by the possibility of a handball tournament was fantastic. It brought huge interest from the different groups of prisoners. Names began to be bantered about to see who would compete. Anyone who was an athlete of any description had his name put forward. These men would represent their own units, so it created a rivalry that made life a little more interesting.

As a footballer my name was included. My father and his family had grown up playing handball in the ball alley in Greene Street. I had played a little in school and I said I would participate. It took my mind off my circumstances and gave me an outlet for my frustrations. The tournament was going to consist of singles and doubles games. We began training for the tournament, one hour a day for three days. Banging the ball about in the yard gave me a great lift. There would be 24 men involved, all the names were put into a hat and drawn out to see who we would be playing against. In the first round of singles, I was up against Jim Dwyer which I won two games out of three.

In the second round I had a tough match against Gerry Daly where I managed to scrape by getting me into the semi-final. The semi was really tough, and I lost to Frank Brennan. For the double games I was paired with John Muldowney who was an accomplished player. We managed to get through to the final against my friend Tom Keogh and Frank Brennan unfortunately we lost out in the final to a very talented pair in two hotly contested games. Even the guards and soldiers had taken an interest and were betting among each other on the outcome.

The tournament itself drew interest outside the prison and there were write ups in local papers about it. Even medals were made specially for the winners with Kilmainham inscribed on them. The medals were valued by the men who won them.

It would take months for the talks to accomplish any positive moves. The dark days of November made for a depressing time in gaol, the dampness and the short days made it hard. I continued with my regime of exercise as much as possible. My mother and Kate had managed to visit me by way of Mrs Redmond's Garden again. It was not ideal, but it was better than nothing. Kate assured me the baby was doing well and would have liked to bring her, but she was still a bit small.

We began to hear rumours of prisoners being released and we were looking forward to that time coming. We knew that Michael Collins, Arthur Griffith was heading the Irish contingent at the Truce negotiations, all we could hope for was a swift end to all of it. At the start of December, we got word of a phased release of the prisoners . We hoped we would be let out by Christmas. The prisoners finally started to be released on the 8th of December in batches of six every half hour starting at 8.00 AM. There were over 200 prisoners released that day. My time came at 11 00 o clock there were crowds gathered outside the prison to greet the released men.

It's hard to describe how I felt walking through that door out to the street, the day was overcast but I had never seen a more welcome sight. The freedom of just walking through a door when you have been locked up is incredible. There were families outside waiting and cheering as we walked out greeting us. As I looked around, I saw Kate standing with my mother and Christy and Uncle Jerry. Kate had a shawl wrapped around her with a small child enclosed within, smiling as I walked towards them. Kate ran to me and lifting the baby towards me said, "This is your daughter Elizabeth, she wants to say hello to her Daddy."

I was dumbstruck, and tears filled my eyes. Never before had I ever had such a feeling of joy. Everyone crowded around me at once and started talking laughing and hugging me. It was like a holiday with everyone cheering and waving as we made our way out. We left the prison in Jerry's pony and trap heading down the Quays to my mams house. Dinah had a feast prepared and all the neighbours were outside to welcome me home. Dinah threw her arms around me at the door wiping away tears as she pulled me into the house. "Look at you," said Dinah "you're as skinny as a rail, we'll have to fix that." Everybody got to enjoy a great breakfast and I got to hold my first-born child.

Going back to our own little flat that day was surreal. It was hard to believe I was going to be living a 'normal' life. Kate's mother was at our flat when we got there, she had a fire lighting, and the room was nice and cosy. We had only been here a short time when I was captured, and I really hadn't got used to being there. It felt good to sit in comfort in a proper chair. "Hello Sam, it's great to have you home, what do you think of this little one?" She said holding Elizabeth up. "Isn't she gorgeous!"

"Yes," I said, "she's beautiful." Mrs Glynn started putting on her coat to leave. "It's Christmas in a couple of weeks. We will have a big party to celebrate you and your family. Thank God your home," Mrs Glynn said as she left.

Being alone with Kate after so long apart felt awkward. Kate was feeding the baby and getting her ready for bed, I just watched fascinated. At five months old she was very active, and I was afraid to hold her. "Are you Ok, Sam?" Kate said, "you don't have to worry everything is going to be alright. It's bound to be a bit strange coming home to a readymade family, we will manage ok. You must be exhausted why don't you lie down while I get Betty to sleep."

"Is that what you call her?" I asked. "Yes! Is that ok? I did call her after your mother."

"Yeah I like it, she will be the apple of my eye once I get used to her." I lay down on the bed thinking about the past months and wondered how I had managed to survive, drifting off to sleep I thanked God for all I had.

I woke up the next morning with Kate beside me. It was our first time spending a whole night together. I woke to Kate breathing softly. After nearly seven months of prison, it took me a while to get used to the normality of it all. After a little while I heard little noises from the cot next to the bed. The baby was starting to wake up, I got out of bed and walked around to have a look. As I gazed at her lying there all cosy and happy I couldn't but help reaching to touch her hand. As soon as I touched her, she opened her eyes and started to cry. I jumped back startled. Then I heard a laugh, Kate had been watching me. "Well," said Kate, "they didn't teach you much about babies in Kilmainham."

"No this is all new," I said. "She is just hungry and needs feeding." Reaching for Betty she took her out and put a shawl around her and started to feed the baby from her breast. I was both embarrassed and fascinated. So many new things I had to get used to. "Why don't you get washed and I will look after the baby," Kate said. "Good idea! I have to report in this morning to my unit."

Kate had the baby sorted and had started making breakfast by the time I was ready. "I can't believe I am here with the two of you."

"Well you are, and you will be always," Kate reached out, and I took her in my arms. I held her close and felt contented for the first time in a long time.

We had been told to report to our own unit when we were released, I walked down to Parnell Square. It was great to walk seeing the bustle of the city as people prepared for Christmas. I arrived at Parnell Square there were men still stationed on watch outside, I didn't recognise them they were new lads. As I came up to them, they asked my business I told them I was reporting in after being released.

"Sorry I didn't mean to hold you up, but we are still taking precaution's just in case. Comdt. Daly is in his office on the top floor go on up." I walked up the staircase thinking so much had happened in such a short time. When I entered the top floor the was a lot of activity, I wasn't the first to arrive, a few of the other men of the ASU were already there. "Sam how are you?" Asked Tom Keogh, "happy to be home?"

"Yes, it's fantastic. It's like a dream, one minute you're in prison next thing you are with your family. It's great," I answered, "What happens now?" The boss is going to talk to us in a few minutes when he is ready Tom said.

We started to chat to each other while we waited. There were six of us that had been in Kilmainham, we talked about how it felt to be out again. The door to Comdt. Daly's office opened. Paddy Daly came out; he was in Volunteer uniform. Another officer I did not know called us to form a line and fall in. We lined up, 'Attention' was called, and we stood straight. Comdt. Daly walked over and stood us at ease. He went down the line and shook the hand of each man greeting us each personally. "Sam it's good to have you back," he said and passed on to the next man. When the formality was over Comdt. Daly told us to sit, we made ourselves comfortable.

"Well men, first of all, it's great to have you back, a lot has happened since we last spoke. Now a lot of you may think that the Custom House was a mistake but let me say it had an impact on the Brits and was instrumental in leading to the Truce that we now have. There are still negotiations going on however, we have to be ready in case things go wrong.

We have more recruits now than we ever had now everybody is joining when there's not as much danger. We still maintain military discipline and you may be asked to train some of the new men. Now you are still part of the ASU and will be paid accordingly. Also, a small grant is given to you men who were in Gaol to help you get by for now. I am sure your families could do with the help. Sgt O'Connor will look after that when we are finished here. He is in the office downstairs.

You will see a lot of new faces around, we had to reorganise after the capture of so many of our best men. The Dublin Brigade supplied the new men. A lot of these men do not have your experience, so bear with them till we get everything up and running. We should know within the next few weeks what is going to happen with the Truce. There is a lot of controversy about it at the moment, we are not politicians we are the Army and we will conduct ourselves as such and be ready if needed. That's it for now, again it's great to have you all back. Dismissed."

After our meeting a few of us decided to go over to the pub on the corner for a drink. We all had our own thoughts of what was now going on, and sooner or later we would have to deal with them. I was not really a drinker as such, but I could manage a pint. The talk of our experience of prison soon drifted to the Truce, basically the stumbling block as far as we were knew, was the wording. In gaol we didn't really know the details. We knew that Michael Collins and Arthur Griffith were part of the negotiation team which seemed strange seeing as De Valera was the top man. It was very confusing.

The North and the Orange Order had split and formed their own Government. They wouldn't have anything to do with us. The country was divided, and people were talking about a choice of Free State or Republic which was the most realistic! The probability of Civil War was making people nervous, had the Irish people not suffered enough. There had to be some solution surely. It was a divisive conversation which brought out the worst in people. "Anyway, lads we are not going to solve anything arguing amongst ourselves let's have a drink and look forward to a Christmas that some of the men we lost won't be having," said Mick Byrne. "Let's enjoy our newfound freedom at least for a little while."

Walking home the conversations kept going around in my head. I walked back to Mountjoy Street enjoying the feel of the city without the threat of being arrested. Kate was waiting when I arrived. "How did it go?" she asked.

"It was good to see the lads and we are still in the Army. I even got a bonus, so I think it's only fair to take my two favourite girls out and buy them a Christmas present."

"Great," said Kate "we are all ready." My mother had gotten a small baby carriage for us, so we put Betty in it and headed for Henry Street. Strolling along with Kate and Betty seemed the most natural thing in the world. We enjoyed our outing, and it was so good seeing the happiness on Kates's face as she picked out items that she and the baby needed.

"While we are out let's go see my Mam and Dinah." So, we started down to East Arran St meeting neighbours who greeted us as we passed by. Dinah opened the door when we arrived, she was so happy to see us, she couldn't wait to get her hands on the baby. My Mam was delighted to see us. It all felt so normal the way most families lived. After being locked up and having lived on the run for more than a year I really needed time to adjust. Would I get it?

Chapter 22
Transition

Christmas came and all the celebrations were enjoyed by everyone. For the first time in four years people had the freedom to visit and celebrate together without being afraid. With the dawning of a new year, we had hoped would come peace. But in January the politicians continued to meet without resolving the split that was occurring within. De Valera and Cathal Brugha took a stand against the Treaty, that was opposed by Collins and Griffith who favoured it. The Treaty would have two separate countries consisting of the Irish Free State, 26 counties in the South, and 6 counties in the North forming Northern Ireland. The country would be partitioned.

The IRA was openly split between the two sides and hope for a breakthrough vanished. A vote was taken in the Dail which saw the vote go in favour of the Treaty by a very small majority. The Irish people wanted peace and now we had a means at our disposal to achieve peace. England would never grant us a Republic and even if she had, the Orangemen in the North would never accept it. Collins looked at the Free State as a steppingstone to a republic in the future, whereas De Valera wanted a return to hostilities in order to try and force a Republic.

A country divided! How was a soldier supposed to decide? We had fought with all we had; we had watched our comrades die in battle. Seen some of our friends executed our country ravaged. We are not philosophers or politicians. Our allegiance is to our country but what is our country. Is it the land or is it the people? It is the 'PEOPLE,' without people there is only ground. So, what do you choose, you choose your comrades the men you depended on when you needed them? The 'Loyalty' to the Organization to which you belonged. And so, I made my decision, I was a Collins man I trusted him to lead us so I will trust him with me and my family's future.

Chapter 23
National Army

A vote was held in Early January with all the delegates of Sinn Fein voting and a decision was made to honour the Treaty, the vote was very close with only a few votes separating the for and against. This was not exactly what we were hoping for. Arthur Griffith and Michael Collins were on the Treaty side while De Velera and Cathal Brugha took the Anti Treaty side. This would lead to division among former comrades and eventually Civil War.

Things began to change The ASU and The Squad were to form the Dublin Guard which would be the first organised unit of the new "National Army," as we were being called.. I was chosen to be part of this new Unit We would be sent to Celbridge to an old Workhouse which we would use as a barracks to train as an Infantry battalion. Eventually we would be issued with the new Grey Green uniform of the Irish Army. We were to become a legitimate Army of Ireland answerable to the newly elected Dail. Paddy Daly would be our C/O and Dick Mulcahy chief of Staff. There was great excitement as we began our training it felt good to be training out in the open with no restrictions. Most of the men were men I had been involved with during the War of Independence made up our first company. We were preparing to take over Beggars Bush Barracks from the British Army which would be the first installation to be handed over to the new National Army.

Collins had wanted a general election to take place which would give the people their say. But De Valera kept stalling. But a split came that caused uncertainty and former comrades began to take different sides. Men I knew were having to choose ,old allegiance's being the deciding factor for most. Either joining up with the Anti-Treaty forces or couldn't make their minds and walked away. My own brother Christy found it difficult to decide, the thoughts of Christy and me being on different side was devastating. But as I said men had to make their own decisions as difficult as they were.

I had been issued with the new grey/green uniform of the new National Army. And was enlisted as a corporal in the Dublin Guard. It felt good to be wearing our own uniform and drilling and training to be a professional soldier. There were former British soldiers now enlisted in the Irish Army, these were Irish men who had fought in the First World War and had returned home.

These men became our trainers and instructors in military discipline and tactics. Part of our duties were guarding public buildings throughout the city. Paddy O Conor was a lieutenant and was in charge of my platoon. Vinny Byrne was our Quarter Master Sargent and I felt privileged to serve with them.

On the 1st of February 1922 were left Celbridge to go to Dublin for the handover of Beggars Bush Barracks. We travelled by Lorry to the Phoenix Park at Park Gate Street where 50 of us formed up in ranks of four and were going to Parade though the city all the way down to Beggars Bush. This was a great and historic occasion . We would be parading as the new Irish Army before the people of Dublin for the first time. Not since the 1916 Rebellion had Irish soldiers marched through the streets in uniform with Flags flying.

We started marching down the Quays led by the Emerald Pipe band being cheered by the people as we went . People had gathered to watch us as we passed all along the route giving us a great welcome as we went .The small contingent marching smartly with sloped arms and bayonets flashing in the sun. As we went by City Hall Michael Collins and Arthur Griffith the President of the Free State gave us a salute. When we reached Beggars Bush a formal hand over was made and we were presented with our Tri Colour flag by Dick Mulcahy. What a day I was so proud to be part of it after all we had endured it felt so good. Kate had managed to see us as we crossed Capel Street bridge her mother and sister were with her and the baby.

As the time dragged on the more difficult it became for soldiers who had fought together to decide what side they were on. I was on guard duty one evening and Vinny came around to each man in the section. "Sam, I have to ask you out straight how you feel about the Treaty?"

I thought for a minute and then responded, "I think that the ordinary people are for it, and I don't think we can do any better at present," I said.

"You know that we may have to fight against men who were our friends, are you prepared to do that?" Vinny asked.

"If it comes to fighting, I will do my bit as I always have. Mick Collins done his best and that's good enough for me," I answered.

"Good," said Vinny "I am glad we can depend on you."

A few weeks later I was sent to the Curragh Camp for officer training. I threw myself into learning and was commissioned as a 1st lieutenant in April 1922 and was assigned back to Portobello Barracks. The National Army had an explosion of recruits, and I became responsible for training my own platoon. I loved the Army life and took to it like a duck to water. By April, the situation in Ireland was awful. The possibility of Civil War became very real, and it wouldn't be against the Unionists of the North, but our own IRA men who had fought all over the country. Matters of principle became more important than common sense.

Anti-Treaty Forces had started occupying key buildings in major towns and cities around the country. There was enormous pressure from the British for the Dail to take control of the situation. We just kept spiralling towards Civil War.

The new Army also took control of buildings and some barracks around the country. In Dublin we were tasked with protecting important buildings in the city. Part of my responsibility was mount guard at College of Surgeons and Leinster House, it was my first time being involved in formal military duty as an officer. In the meantime, Anti-Treaty forces had occupied the Four Courts under the command of Rory O'Connor who had been a close associate of Michael Collins.

Kate and I were still in Mountjoy Street. Betty was almost a year old. Time had passed so quickly. Because I lived locally, I was able to stay at home and travel to the barracks daily. Kate was so proud of me now an officer in the Army she said I looked very handsome in my new uniform. Our baby Betty had not been well lately, and we were worried about her. There was something wrong with her back and she sometimes had difficulty breathing.

Kate took her to the hospital, and we found she had bad asthma and a problem with her spine which was not as straight as it should be. They told us not to worry as she might grow out of it. We took the advice of the doctors and kept a good eye on Betty. She was such a little beauty with her big brown eyes, jet black hair and dark complexion we loved her to bits. It wasn't too long before she was able to crawl around the floor and gave us such enjoyment just watching her.

Chapter 24
Civil War

Things took a turn for the worst when the British government insisted that the Irregular forces occupying buildings in the country should be forcibly removed. They threatened to end the Treaty and commence hostilities against the Rebels. The die was cast and reluctantly Dick Mulcahy Minister of Defence gave the order to start offensive action against the Four Courts Garrison and other buildings in Dublin that Rebel forces had seized. A plan was drawn up by Emmet Dalton which involved two 18 pounder field guns loaned by the British to our Army to shell the building. A large force now was entrenched in the Four Courts and surrounding buildings, which would make an infantry assault very costly.

These guns would be used to bombard the Four Courts. On the night of the 27th of June 1922 in the early hours of the morning, the Irish Civil war began. The National Army as we were now known began to fire artillery shells across the river from Wine Tavern St This was our first time to use heavy guns. We did not have fully qualified gunners and had to use men with limited experience, so it took a while to begin to fire accurately at the buildings.

The Rebels inside replied with rifle and machine gun fire, but it wasn't that effective, there were some men wounded. It was awful to think we were shelling our own people. The shelling would continue for two days. In the meantime, other areas of the city were occupied by the Anti-Treaty forces. Mainly they had taken buildings along O'Connell Street. I was with one of the platoons sent to take back these buildings. The National Army as we were now known deployed my battalion, the Dublin Guard, to deal with this situation. I was in charge of a squad of twenty men with two NCO's. It would be our job to make our way along Parnell Street towards O'Connell Street and link up with other units to clear the buildings and take back control of the city.

Of the twenty men most were armed with Lee-Enfield rifles We had 1 section with a Lewis machine gun, we also had grenades. As we moved along Parnell Street, we came under fire from snipers. It was necessary to deploy the Lewis gun and a section to deal with these strong points. We got about halfway along Parnell Street when a machine gun opened up on us from the roof of a building near the Rotunda Hospital in Parnell Square. They also had snipers placed in windows and on roof tops. We had to retreat and try to regroup to move around the laneways at the back of the main street in order to try and get close to them.

This was my first time in a sustained firefight, and I was now responsible for the men under my command. I felt that to be a heavy burden. I decided we would be cautious and advance slowly. I sent out scouts to draw fire and then concentrated the Lewis gun on the most dangerous targets. The men I had were mostly new recruits with little or no experience of war. This was a baptism of fire and it was going to define the strength of our resolve. The more experienced men had to set an example for the others.

I sent Tom McCarthy, one of my sergeants, to see if we could get another Lewis gun. He returned with two Thompson Guns with extra ammunition. This gave us extra fire power and should give us an edge. We would be able to leapfrog along on both sides of the street. I took one of the Thompsons which I was familiar with and Tom took the other one. As soon as we saw a target I would engage with the Thompson while a couple of my better men would move in for a better shot with our rifles. That way we began a slow deliberate advance toward O'Connell Street.

Like our own troops the Rebels were also using a lot of new inexperienced men. They tended to rush their attacks and were not as accurate as they could have been , so we began to make progress. By nightfall we had advanced almost up to Parnell Square. We would hold up here till daylight. I posted guards while the men rested and got some food. We were not equipped to provide properly for our men, so we had to go into shops and even the pubs to get food for our men. Some of the families brought food to their men fighting in the streets. Kate's mother was in Dominick Street and she brought sandwiches and tea down to my men.

I am not sure how I felt after our first action. I thought I had kept calm and conducted myself properly. In the heat of battle your training and adrenaline takes over and you're just reacting to the situation you are in. But after when you sit and think it's a whole different story. Here I was fighting against my own people, some who had been with me fighting against the British. It was a sad feeling to think I could actually kill men who had been my friends.

Even my own brother could be on the other side I was not sure. I had not seen Christy for a few weeks and did not know which side he had joined. There had been so much confusion prior to the outbreak of hostilities. Men had changed sides several times already depending on where their loyalty lay. I don't know who came up with the name 'Civil' War there is nothing civil about war.

The fighting along Parnell Street resumed with first light the following day. The Rebels were well entrenched in some of the buildings around Parnell Square. I had some men working their way along the rooftops now to try to engage the snipers, while the men on the street continued to work our way along. The biggest problem was the machine gun at the corner of Fredrick Street he had a clear view of any movement on Parnell Street. I went back to see our C/O Joe Leonard to discuss our options, he had more men working their way along Henry Street beside the GPO. The Rebels were in and around the Gresham Hotel and another hotel the Hamman.

They had a commanding field of fire because of the tall buildings. It was decided to bring up an artillery piece to try to dislodge the Rebels. When the 18 Pounder arrived, it began to shell the rebel held buildings with incendiary shells and soon the buildings were on fire. Once the heavy firepower began it was the beginning of the end for the rebels. They began to retreat, and some were captured trying to escape the flames. Then we heard that the Four Courts had had a huge explosion where it's thought a large land mine had exploded within.

The Garrison there had surrendered. The field gun we had fired at the machine gun position at the corner of Fredrick Street caused considerable damage to the building. The machine gun withdrew and disappeared. Without the machine gun we could move up to link with the other Army men and force the surrender of the Rebels. Cathal Brugha who was commanding the men in the Gresham Hotel decided to fight a rear-guard action to protect his men who were trying to escape. When all his men had left, Brugha came out of the burning building which was now surrounded by our forces, his clothing was scorched his face covered with grime from the smoke, with guns in both hands he began to advance towards the waiting troops. When called to surrender by both sides, he ran at our soldiers firing and was shot dead. It was a hollow victory to see such iconic figure mown down by his own countrymen.

There was a feeling of sadness among all the men that witnessed this sacrifice. Oscar Traynor who was the Commander of Rebel forces withdrew all of his men; the Battle of Dublin was over! With the surrender of the Rebel forces in the city the Army became busy with rounding up any remaining Anti-Treaty troops. We had lost a few men and had a lot of men wounded. Again, it seemed the brunt of the battle was borne by civilian casualties.

I returned home on the 6th of July for a couple of days leave. Kate was relieved to see me as she had been kept awake by the sounds of the battle only 800 yards away. I needed to rest and come to terms of what I had been through. My first thoughts were that I had acquitted myself well in the battle and had gained valuable experience in urban warfare. My men would now be ready for our next action and would have confidence in our ability to survive. "Are you all right Sam?" Kate asked.

"Yes love, I am ok. It was very hard at first to realise you are fighting your own people ,but when bullets start whizzing around you learn fast."

"How long are you home for?" Kate asked.

"A couple of days and then more training."

"Well let's make the best of them so, the baby's asleep and you need a rest," said Kate taking my hand and leading me to the bed.

A few days later I got some good news, Christy had joined up in the National Army with the 27th Battalion, which was based for the time being in the Curragh .He sent a note up to me with a friend who was coming up to HQ in Portobello. It read, "Hi Sam, I just wanted to let you know I am Ok. I heard you were worried about me.

Believe me this was a tough decision as you well know. More than half my company sided with the Anti Treaty side. I almost joined them in O'Connell Street, I even had a rifle in my hand before things started. Seeing your pals so confused and listening to the rhetoric of the higher ups is what pushed me over the edge. The ordinary people want peace and after all that's what we set out to get. So, I am sure we will meet up in time. I am in officer training at the moment. I sent a letter to Mam so she wouldn't worry. Some people told me you were seen in Parnell Street. I am glad you got out OK. See you soon. Christy."

A weight had lifted off my shoulders.

Chapter 25
The Offensive

After a couple of days rest it was back to training, the realisation of having so many inexperienced troops caused some anxiety in the command structure. It was decided to build a first-class battalion within the Dublin Guard that could be sent to the most contested areas. The Anti-Treaty Forces had headed south to Munster where they had the most support. Our forces were building up with the addition of armoured cars and some artillery. After the defeat in Dublin the Rebels would be reluctant to occupy large towns or buildings.

The prospects of a drawn-out guerrilla war across the southern counties was daunting. Our commanders will have to come up with some different plans. On the 6th of July a contingent of 400 troops supported by 4 armoured cars and 1 field gun headed south from Dublin to Wexford lead by Col. Keogh to secure Wexford and Waterford. Another larger force headed for Limerick, 1500 strong with armoured cars and a field gun led by Major General Eoin O'Duffy. These troops were mostly green with little battle experience. They were up against a disciplined and battle-hardened force.

This force entered Limerick on July 17th. After some initial fighting in the city the Rebel forces retired south and set up defences south of the city around three villages near Burree. The Rebel Forces were led by Liam Deasy and were strengthened by units from Kerry and Cork. The largest battle of the Civil War occurred when the National Army advanced south. It was a battle with use of heavy weapons and upwards of 2000 men. The National Army finally won a victory, when reinforced by new troops and then on August 2nd when more troops landed in Kerry and Cork the Rebel forces disbanded and retired to their own counties.

On August 2nd, Cork City was the objective that would be the most important target. A plan to bypass the overland route to Cork was devised by Emmet

Dalton. Sea borne landings were to be carried out to eliminate the need to pass through heavy defences around larger towns. Large ships capable of carrying troops the Arvonia and the SS Lady Wicklow were acquired. Troops were trained for the operation which Started landing troops in Fenit, County Kerry on August 2nd. The Dublin Guard would be one of the units involved.

Sea borne landings had already taken place previously in Clew Bay in Mayo at the town of Westport. A force of 400 Free State soldiers including an armoured car and field gun landed on 24th July. The Town was retaken without much fighting and another force under General Sean Mc Eoin was also dispatched to Castlebar and forced the dispersal of the IRA units in the Galway and Mayo.

The next objective was the so-called Munster Republic which consisted of the counties of Cork, Kerry, Tipperary and Limerick. The Dublin Guard landed in Fenit Co. Kerry on Aug 2nd with General Paddy Daly in charge. When we landed, we were in a completely different environment to that we were used to. We had been used to fighting in a built-up area, now we had to adjust to fighting in country lanes and open country.

Our battalion was equipped with two armoured cars and one field gun. More troops arrived from Clare via Tarbert giving us about 500 soldiers. In the face of this strong force the rebels began a policy of hit and run attacks. However, these attacks although causing casualties on both sides could not stop us taking over the all the major towns. As I said before when the skirmishes began training takes over and you become a soldier where you will respond with the same ferocity as the attackers. On both sides atrocities occurred which caused bitterness and hate. The hardest thing I found was the way some of the local population regarded us.

We were being compared to the Black and Tans by supporters of the Anti-Treaty families. Given the nickname 'Staters.' We believed we had the support of most of the Irish people who only wanted peace and a chance to live in a free country.

On August 8th Emmet Dalton landed troops in Passage West in Cork and more in Youghal. After some heavy fighting around Douglas and Rochestown, the Rebels retreated into Cork City. The National Army entered Cork City unopposed on Aug 10th, to save the destruction of the city which had been badly damaged by the Black and Tans the previous year. The National Army set up headquarters in Cork City. While fighting down through Kerry on August 12th we got news of the sudden death of the President Arthur Griffith.

This was blow to our provisional Government only newly formed. We suspended operations and went to Cork City to establish control of the area. Most of the commanders would go to Dublin for the State funeral of the president. I was billeted with the other officers in my battalion in the Imperial Hotel in Cork City.

The National Army had taken control of most of the country. There were still pockets of resistance, especially the southern part around West Cork and Kerry. After the Funeral of Arthur Griffith, Michael Collins decided to make an inspection tour of the deployment of the Army. Travelling through the country in convoy in an open car with an armoured car and a lorry with soldiers. He visited with Army Garrisons on his way down to Cork City. He arrived in Cork on Monday 21st August and met with officers in the Imperial Hotel, where he stayed overnight.

The following morning Wednesday August 22nd all the officers were at breakfast in the Imperial Hotel. General Michael Collins entered the dining with his usual whirlwind style calling out to well-known associates and greeting friends. He was accompanied by General Dalton and General Paddy Daly. He moved among the seated men, shaking hands and talking. I was privileged to have my hand shook with a smile and acknowledged as a 'Good Lad'. There was a feeling of success in the air. There were no speeches just an appreciation of the job we were doing. As a young officer I thought it felt good to be part of the Army.

Generals Collins and Dalton were leaving, and we were told heading down to West Cork which was Collins own part of the country. They had an armoured car and extra troops for protection. Nobody expected any major problems. I had some work to do preparing for our next move into Co. Kerry. We would be going to Listowel to take over the town. Towards nightfall as we were in the officer's mess Paddy Daly came in, he looked shocked and pale. He announced in an almost inaudible voice that Michael Collins had been killed in an ambush at Beal na Blath in West Cork, not far from his own home.

We were stunned. How could this happen! Such a dynamic person; shot with so many of us in the vicinity. Soon the shock would become anger but for the moment it was hard to take in. There were no details of the ambush other than General Collins was the only casualty. This incident would become, in time, one of the most controversial occurrences of the entire Civil War. I felt awful, I looked on him as such a great man, a man of destiny who I thought would in time deliver the freedom our country deserved. A man that was loved and admired as much by his enemies and his friends. In two short weeks, we had lost two of the most important men in modern Irish history.

The officers of the Dublin Guard, most of whom were former Squad and ASU member myself included went to Dublin to be part of a guard of honour at the funeral of Michael Collins. Thousands of people lined the streets to pay their respects as we walked in procession with our own bitter thoughts and fond memories. A pall of sadness hung over the city. Thousands of people lined the streets of the funeral cortege, some weeping openly. Kate stood with her family watching as we passed by. After the funeral I had a couple of days at home before I was to return to Cork. I went to visit my mother.

I hadn't had any word from Christy for a while and was wondering if Ma had heard from him. She told me he had been in touch and now serving with General Sean Mc Eoin in Mayo. It was nice to be home with Kate and Betty. Even in this loving environment it was hard to shake off the melancholy I felt. But we had a job to do, and we had to honour our dead leader by seeing it through. We left by train for Cork on Friday morning. I was accompanied by several officers of The Guard, there was a lot of talk of what would happen now Collins was gone.

We had always felt he was the one most likely to end this conflict as he was respected by leaders on both sides. The new provisional Government were not well known to us. We knew President Cosgrave had been in the Rising and had been in the Volunteers, but we had no idea what his policies might be.

After arriving in Cork City, I was told to join my unit in Listowel. I reported to Col. Joe Leonard who was in charge temporarily while General Daly was in Dublin. We would be continuing operations against a flying column which was operating in the area. I was called in to see the C/O Paddy Daly the following week. "Hello Sam, how are you doing? Terrible business with the boss," he said.

"Yes, Sir," I answered.

"They will pay a heavy price if I have anything to do with it," he said with an edge to his voice. "I wanted to talk to you, I am transferring yourself and 3 other officers to the 26th battalion who just arrived down here. They are mostly new troops and they don't have many combat experienced officers. The C/O is Jack Callahan he was a volunteer in Monaghan He has some experience but needs help. Once you get them in shape you can come back here OK."

"Yes, Sir. When do I report, Sir?"

"Tomorrow, they are over at Tarbert. They just crossed over from Clare. A car will take you fellas up and good luck." I went to get my gear, on the way I met Bill O'Brien, one of the officers going with us.

"What do you think Sam, will we miss this lot?" He said laughing. I said, "we might get a rest."

The next morning the four officers left Listowel for Tarbert by car. Three of us were old ASU men and one new man. He was a young lad just out of the Curragh camp training centre, Jim Brady was his name. He was probably the same age as me but looked 14 years old. We reported to Comdt. Callahan The troops were unloading supplies from a ship, they had an armoured car and an 18-pounder artillery piece. The battalion had about 250 men. Comdt. Callahan told us we were to move out and head south of Listowel where we would establish a HQ camp. I was assigned with Lieut. Brady to B Company.

We had some experienced Non-Com's who knew the drill and organised the troops. We would route march to our destination while all our supplies would be carried on trucks. We had some outriders on motorcycles who would scout ahead for any enemy activity. The roads in Kerry are very narrow and the landscape for the most part is mountainous and some rolling hills. This type of terrain is ideal for ambush we would have to be on our toes especially in any kind of valley. It was going to be slow moving the whole battalion through this area.

We sent the armoured car and a lorry with troops about ½ a mile ahead. Comdt. Callahan had us sweep the countryside on both sides of the column in case we were surprised by hostiles. It would be late when we set up temporary camp just north of Listowel. I set up our platoon on the west side of the column while Frank Burke was on the east side. This was all new to most of the troops and we needed to constantly remind them that this was no exercise. Thank God we had decent NCO's. Lying in the grass that night in the mild September evening it was no wonder some men thought they were on holiday, the area was beautiful and scenic. I had never been so far south before; it would be a lovely place to visit in peace time. Sentries were placed around the camp and we settled in for the night.

We broke camp the next morning and continued south. The local people watched us pass without acknowledging us. We were in 'Bandit' country although we hadn't made any contact. In Listowel we made contact with some forward observers who warned us to be alert. At the Guard HQ, it had been quiet for a few days. Some of our men had sore feet already; they had a lot to look forward to. After being issued rations, we set off again following the same order of march. We arrived at our new camp location about 15 miles south of Listowel on the way to Tralee.

We set up camp in the village of Crotta Cross, near a crossroads that would give us access to roads east and west. We took over a big house that had been destroyed near the crossroads and set up our tents in the surrounding fields. This would be our main base where we could monitor any activity. It was on high ground and we could see all the way to the Atlantic in the distance. Once we got settled, we would begin patrolling the surrounding area looking for Rebel troops.

Chapter 26
Battle of Rathmore

September 6th saw us settled in camp with a routine of patrols around the roads leading down to Tralee and up towards Listowel. So far, we had not encountered any resistance from Rebel forces. The area consisted mostly of small farms. The terrain favoured sheep as the foothills leading into the mountain was ideal for them. We would visit some of the farms and search for weapons or set up roadblocks and search any vehicles or farm carts passing through. The general population kept to themselves and avoided contact with us. Trying to maintain discipline was challenging as men got bored with the same thing most days.

Comdt. Callahan wanted to send a large patrol into the mountain to sweep the area to see if we could flush out the enemy. Intelligence information said there was a flying column in the vicinity. My company was designated for this operation. Because the roads were poor, in some cases just mountain tracks, we would not have any heavy weapons, other than Lewis guns rifles and Grenades. The armoured car would be on standby along the road in case it was needed. Three platoons of 30 men each would form the makeup of our force. Capt. Clarke in command, we spread out at 200-yard intervals, whichever platoon made contact would send a runner for reinforcements. It was a plan more suitable to open ground rather than hilly terrain.

We started out at first light on September 10th all the troops had full gear including great coats as the morning was damp it had rained the night before. Platoons were broken down to 10 men sections each with a Lewis gun and an NCO. I had Lieut. Brady with me. I covered the right flank with Frank Burke on the left and Capt. Clarke in the centre. What had started as a damp morning turned into a lovely sunny day. It felt more like a walk in the woods rather than a search for the enemy. There was a scrubby pine forest at the base of the first hill.

As we moved through, we thought we heard movement but could not see anyone. We could hear shouting out to our left. When we came out of the forest we could see some movement on the left flank, there were a few men making their way up into a craggy little valley about half a mile in front. Lieut. Burkes men were closest and started to pursue the men, long range shots were exchanged without any casualties. They're running Lieut. Burke shouted his platoon immediately started after the fleeing figures. Capt. Clarke ordered his men to assist Lieut. Burke. This made it hard for my platoon as we now had a large gap between us.

I shouted to my platoon to spread out and try to keep contact with the others. As we reached the crest of the hill there was a flat plain. The first and second platoon were now almost halfway across when all hell broke loose. Machine gun and rifle fire rained down on the forward platoons some men fell as they raced for cover. The machine gun was well sighted and was creating havoc. There was a ridge along the side of the mountain and the Rebel force was entrenched behind it giving them perfect cover and a perfect field of fire. We had run into a trap. I shouted to my sections to, *"Take Cover!"*

We jumped down behind the crest of the ridge and we started to return fire with the Lewis guns. Before we had even got down behind cover, bullets were singing around us, and we had a couple of men hit in the first minute. Luckily, we were a little spread out, otherwise we have suffered more casualties. I could see men lying out in the open where they had been caught in the initial fire. The rest were trying to make it back to safety behind the crest of the hill.

"Ok lads rapid fire across that ridge. We have to try cover Capt. Clarke's men. Just try to pin them down. Shoot at the bushes along the ridge, that's where they will be," I shouted. The valley resounded to the sounds of rifle and machine gun fire.

A runner came from Capt. Clarke to me, "The Captain wants you to see if you can get someone out to get help."

I looked around. We were closest to the forest. "Keep firing at that machine Gun I shouted to our Lewis gun we have to try pin him down till the others get back to cover. Meanwhile I had an NCO who was a very fit lad Jack Brennan," I told him. "I need you to break out of here and get help, you might make contact by the road, leave all your gear and run like hell OK."

"Yes, Sir." Dropping his gear, I handed him my revolver and wished him luck. He took off like a hare and was into the forest before they got the range on him. Bullets tore into the trees after him as he charged down the hill. We were pinned down, we had to worry about snipers getting down around the flank and taking us from the rear. The force against was a much larger force than we had anticipated, and they were well disciplined.

I shouted to Sergeant Farrell, "Take one of the Lewis guns and a section to guard our flank." He grabbed the Lewis gun and his section moved to form a defensive line on our right side. We waited as the firing continued, so far, the Rebels had not made any forward movement. They were content to engage us where we were as they had the advantage of height plus the bright sun illuminated our position. In order for us to disengage we would have to expose ourselves to heavy fire. So, a stalemate ensued as we waited.

The NCO I sent to contact the armoured car came out onto the road at a dead run. Lucky for him there was one of our motorcycle patrols with side car out patrolling on the road , they had heard the firing echoing in the hills and were trying to see where it was coming from. They sped back to camp. Col. Callahan immediately got a couple of lorry loads of men and the artillery piece and headed out towards us. The sun had risen, and the battlefield was very hot. Our position was bad and we couldn't move without drawing fire. We had wounded and dead men all over the battlefield. Then to make things worse the Rebels begun to move around our flank. Fortunately, I had set up a Lewis gun on that side and we started to fire on them. A savage firefight ensued, and we would have been overrun but for the courage and bravery of that section. Once the Rebels halted their attack on our flank the rest of the company tried to regroup. As we were getting organised, we heard the crack of an artillery shell flying over our heads, Brennan had got through. It was a welcome sound, it crashed into the mountain above the Rebels.

It would not be too long before they got the range. Several shells rained down on the mountain causing The Rebels to retreat in the face of artillery fire. They disappeared into the mountains.

As the firing stopped, we started to see the damage that had been done, we had 7 men killed and nearly two dozen injured some seriously, Comdt. Callahan came to the field to see for himself. This was one of the worst defeats we had suffered so far. For a lot of our men this was a Baptism of fire. A lot of the young soldiers looked dazed as they arrived back at Camp. Today was day they would never forget.

The dead and wounded were loaded onto trucks and taken back to Listowel, the dead to be brought back to Dublin, the wounded would be treated locally. When we got back to our billets, I was taking off my great coat and noticed two bullet holes in the bottom of my coat where it had lain open on the ground. The Battle of Rathmore was over. Lessons were learned that day, the Rebels were far more deadly than they had been given credit for, and our intelligence was shite. "The Flying Column" had become a Battalion.

While we continued to patrol around the area we did so with support of the armoured car and motor transport. September turned out to be one of the worst months for us so far. On the 16th of September a convoy of the Dublin Guard soldiers travelling from Macroom in Cork to Tralee in Kerry were investigating a large land mine that was found blocking their way. Tom Keogh and four other ex-Squad members were in the convoy. Tom was experienced with explosive devices and disconnected some cables that were attached. Thinking they had defused the mine; the men lifted the mine which was booby trapped.

It exploded, killing eight tearing them to pieces and wounding several more, including Tom who died later that evening of his wounds. It was reported that an IRA prisoner was shot by Army in retaliation. I was devastated when I heard the news. I had known Tom since I joined up and had been with him in the Custom House and in Kilmainham. It was a tragedy.

Tit for tat killing became routine, it was wearing us down. The new provisional Government took a much different approach than had been the case with Griffith and Collins. Arrests and internment became prevalent, and executions were frequent. What was the justification? Yes, they were Anti-Treaty, but will there be no end to the killing. Surely a way could be found to stop the destruction of our country. We continued with operation into the winter months. Conditions were tough as we had no permanent barracks. As we moved from town to town, we would billet our troops in any large buildings that were available. Tents in an Irish winter are not ideal. In December I got word I was to report back to Dublin for reassignment. I wasn't sorry to leave Kerry behind. I had lost some brave and true friends.

Chapter 27
Special Infantry Corp

Returning to Dublin in December was a welcome respite. I had been in the field now for 4 months and I felt tired and a little disillusioned. The war was dragging on with no end to the bitterness that had developed. All I could hope for was that the leaders on both sides would resolve the situation. In the meantime, I would continue to serve the best way I could. Kate and Betty would be delighted to have me home. As I boarded the train from Limerick, I wondered what now lay in store for me.

I arrived at Kingsbridge Station in the late afternoon, I hadn't had time to let my family know I was on my way home. I decided to surprise them by just showing up. Walking through the city was so different than the small back roads and lanes of the country, where any moment you could walk into an ambush. The city was bustling, Guinness barges were in the river bringing beer down to the docks. There was a lot of motorised traffic along the Quays with trams operating all along the way. I hopped on a tram as far as O'Connell Street. The Main Street was still in ruins but at least it had been cleaned up and looked as if there was some restoration going on. Beside the GPO on Henry Street shoppers were going about their business, giving the place an air of normality.

When I got to our house on Mountjoy Street, I walked up to the door and knocked. I could hear a voice inside; Kate answered the door. "Oh my god! Sam is it really you?" She said, throwing her arms around me.

"Yes, it's me," I replied "It's great to be home."

"Why didn't you let me know you were coming home? Look at the state of me," said Kate smoothing her pinney.

"You look good to me," I said. Then I noticed a little toddler on the floor standing up holding on to a chair, her dark hair and big brown eyes looked at me. Then she toddled over to her Mam on unsteady legs, clinging to her mother's skirt she buried her face in it. Betty had started to walk while I was away. Kate lifted Betty up and held her in her arm while we all hugged each other. We were a family again.

"Look Betty, Daddy's home," said Kate showing Betty to me. I wasn't sure if I should try to take her as she didn't know me well enough yet, she clung to her Mam. I would have to get to know this little beauty all over again.

Kate fussed around making us dinner I was content just to watch, breathing in a feeling of happiness. Betty had gotten used to seeing me and would look up at me smile and then hide away again. Kate said, "Does your Mam know your home?"

"No, I came straight here; I'll go down and see her tomorrow. I wanted to see you first."

"You look tired. Was it bad down there? We heard all kinds of thing were happening?"

"Yes, it was. It was brutal. I lost some good friends, you heard about Tom Keogh. That was awful. Our lads were very upset when that happened. I thought they would go on a rampage. One man was shot, fortunately it wasn't more. I was sickened when I heard about the bomb! Eight men blown to bits. Anyway, let's forget about all that for now. I am glad to be back for a little while. Any word of Christy?" I asked.

"Your Mam was saying he was in Waterford last she heard," Kate replied.

"I have to report to Portobello on Monday to find out about my new job. We will enjoy ourselves till then, so we have the next few days together."

Next morning waking to smells of cooking in a warm bed was great. Kate came over and kissed me. "Are you getting up today? You've been asleep all morning."

"I could sleep longer if you were in here with me," I said. "Go off out of that you, we have a child to mind," she said with a grin. Now I knew I was home. After lunch time we went down to my Mam's house, she usually didn't get home till after one o'clock. She was walking up the street when we surprised her. She was delighted to see us. "Where did you come from? It's good to see you, son, are you OK?"

"Yeah I'm fine Ma, glad to be home."

"Come on, Dinah will have a fit if we don't go in right away," Ma said. Sure enough when Dinah saw us, she was over the moon. "Well, Sam Robinson, let me look at you. You look a bit skinny, does that Army not feed you?" said Dinah.

"Not like you do Dinah, what have you got that's nice," I said. The meal as usual was scrumptious and Dinah was in her alley having someone to look after. When we were leaving, we had to promise to come to dinner on the Sunday.

The next couple of days were surreal after being away. Doing normal things, going shopping and meeting family and friends. "I will have to get a new uniform," I said to Kate "This one got destroyed. I can keep it for out in the field."

Kate said, "You know that shop on Capel Street, near Mary Street, they make uniforms for officers now, I seen them in the window. They're lovely you could go there."

"We can go out after and have a look," I replied. We went out later that day to Louis Copelands men's outfitters and I ordered my first handmade uniform. It would take a few days to be made and Louis, as I came to know him by, gave me a special price as I was one of his first army customers. So, when I reported to Portobello the next week, I had a smart new uniform.

When I reported to Portobello, I was told I would be going to the Special Infantry Group serving under Col. Joe Byrne, he had his HQ in The Curragh. I was given leave till the new year and was told to report on Jan 1st to the Curragh camp. It was now the 19th of December. I could look forward to being home for almost two weeks, I knew a lot of people who would be glad. The Curragh was close enough to Dublin, I might even be able to get the odd weekend pass. I would use the time I had to enjoy being home. The Christmas holidays came. I enjoyed my first Christmas in my own home as a father with my new family. It was great to see all the family time flew by. The time at home gave me new energy and when I reported back I was well rested and ready.

Chapter 28
New Assignment

I took the train to Kildare and was picked up at the station and transported to the Curragh with several officers who were also reporting for training and new duty. I found Col. Byrnes HQ and went in. There was a Comdt. in the office doing some paperwork with a Sergeant. I approached him and saluted "Lieut. Robinson reporting," I said.

"Hello Sam, how are you?" It was then I recognised former Squad member Paddy Conroy. "Jeepers, Paddy. Sorry Sir, I didn't recognise you."

"That's Ok," he said and returned my salute. "I am only getting used to all these formal military ways myself," he said. "Come on through and I will introduce you to the Colonel." We entered the office of Col. Byrne. "Good morning Sir, this is Lieut. Sam Robinson reporting for duty," Conroy said.

"Welcome Sam. Glad to have you," said Col Byrne. "I see you are one of his bunch," he said with a smile. "There are a few of you down here now. Paddy will tell all you need to know. We are just getting ready for operations which will involve assisting civil powers such as courts and police to try and get this country up and running. You will be promoted to the rank of temporary Captain and have a company in Paddy's 5th battalion. We have a lot of new recruits, and it is going to take a lot of training to get them ready. This assignment will be a lot different than you have been doing. It's Kevin O'Higgins, the Government Ministers, idea. They are concerned about lawlessness which seems to be happening all over with the lack of a proper police force yet. We will have a proper plan laid out within the next couple of weeks. In the meantime, Paddy will get you organised. Welcome Aboard."

I saluted and said, "Thank you Sir."

It took a little while to settle in. I was now a Company commander of C Co. 5th battalion, with 150 men under my command, most of whom was their first time under military discipline. This was going to be a challenging task. I was still only a kid in the eyes of some people, I would have to earn the respect of those who didn't know me. Having been an athlete I was still in very good shape, so I began with physical fitness for the company. I had three senior Lieutenants and three junior Lieutenants, an assortment of NCO's. The NCO's, always the backbone of any army, were the key to success.

I was fortunate. Some of my NCO's were men I already knew, and some had experienced action in Dublin and the southwest. We got to work training the men, first close order drill, running and route marches; by the time they got to bed at night they were too tired to complain. After a couple of weeks, they started to jell together and resembled a military unit. We still had a way to go, we were to be deployed at the end of the month. My second in command Bill Fitzsimons an Irishman who had been a British soldier and had seen service in WW1. Although older than me he had no problem with me being younger. "What do you think Bill?" I asked.

"They are starting to shape up, another few days and they'll look like soldiers."

"Do you know where we are going yet?" Bill asked.

"Rumour has it we will be in the Northwest somewhere; we will have to wait and see. We should know fairly soon." I answered. "They are out on the range tomorrow we will see how they do, then we can get organised."

A meeting of all officers was called by Col. Byrne brigade C/O and Comdt. Conroy. battalion commander. "Gentlemen we are now ready to deploy. We have three companies ready to go and another that will be a reserve unit. We are moving into the Northwest and we have responsibility for Galway Mayo and Sligo. A company will be in Galway, B company in Mayo and C company in Sligo. We will make our HQ in Athlone and the reserve battalion will be based there to assist where needed, also they will be responsible for supplies. Each company will have their own transport lorries and motorcycles with side cars armed with a Lewis gun for rapid response if needed."

"We should not need heavy weapons but if attacked by irregular forces we will have a heavy battalion located in Athlone Barracks available to help. Our mission is to restore order in these counties which has been out of control with no police in place. People have been occupying land and stealing cattle and generally causing havoc. There are still a lot of weapons out there and people that know how to use them."

"Also, they have a lot of support from Irregular forces. Anywhere there are courts available we will use them and assist the Garda when they need us, we have the powers of arrest and detention. We will meet force with force where necessary. Our goal is to start to restore normality around the country. That's it, Gentlemen, we will start moving on Monday morning. You can have weekend passes for the troops then we get down to business. Comdt. Conroy will have you your orders when you get back on Monday."

I took the train to Dublin with the other officers and men. Being the C/O of the company, I had to maintain a certain distance from the men as I would be responsible to maintain discipline in the future. This was new to me and took some getting used to. Leaving the station, I thought about way things had changed in just a year. I had gone through battles, seen friends die and maimed and now was about to start a whole new episode of my Army career. I was now a professional Officer, and I was just 19 years old. Seeing everybody for the weekend was great it took my mind of the upcoming campaign. Kate and Betty were delighted to have me home. And I now learned I was going to be a father again in June, Kate was three months pregnant. "What do you think about the new baby?" Kate asked.

"It's great I hope you will be Ok here. I could be away for a while," I answered.

"Don't worry we will be fine. Mammy is close by and your Mam is very good to us. You just be careful I saw those bullet holes in your old great coat," Kate said.

"I didn't notice them till the next day, this new job is different so it should not be as dangerous. We will be operating more like a police force than a fighting force," I told her.

"Come on, let's go out and celebrate. Ask Maggie to mind Betty and we will go out and enjoy ourselves," I said. We arranged for Maggie to come over. Kate got all dressed up, I had my new uniform on, and we went out to The Royal and had a great night out. It felt really good meeting friends and enjoying ourselves. Sunday night I took the train back to The Curragh wondering if I would be up to the task, I was about to face.

Chapter 29
C Company

Monday morning found the 5th Battalion all assembled on the Parade ground in companies being inspected by our Brigadier General Joe Dalton. We would be one of the first battalions of the Special Infantry to be deployed. After the inspection Comdt. Conroy issued orders to us, C company was to be sent to Sligo town where we would conduct operations in the Northwest counties. We travelled by train to Athlone. From there each of the companies would head to their designated areas. Our company started out we spent a couple of days in Athlone getting all our equipment organised.

We would head north through Mayo and Roscommon into Sligo. Going through Co. Mayo, we came to the town of Knock we were told about how some of the townspeople had seen an apparition of 'Our Lady' on the gable end of the church building some years before. It had now become a place of pilgrimage. We stopped at the church to see where this miracle had taken place. Some of the people who had experienced this vision were still in the town we were told. We had to break up the convoy with motorcycles out in front with two lorries full of troops in case of trouble, then we could bring on the rest of the convoy. I had an open-air car which held six of us. We kept everything moving, the roads were narrow and some in bad repair, when passing through villages or small towns we became congested and had to slow right down direct traffic through the narrow streets.

The local people in some places were happy to see us, others gave us dirty looks as if we were an army of occupation. It was slow going and took a whole day to reach Sligo town. We were going to take over an old barracks in the town which would become our base. Once we got set up, we could begin our operations.

The old barracks was in poor shape and we had to do a fair amount of work to make it comfortable. As soon as I could I made myself known to the mayor of the town John Mc Bride. He was a supporter of the new provisional Government and was glad to see us. Most of the problems were occurring outside of the town in smaller villages and in the country. There were some problems we heard with strikes that were happening which caused problems for everybody. This was going to be a learning experience for us we needed some expert advice.

I was lucky there was a couple of lawyers and a judge in the town, so the mayor set up a committee to hear complaints from the local people. The local priests were also a good source of information. I designated one of my senior Lieutenants Bob Mulhall as a liaison officer. I told him, "Bob you are more able to speak to this committee than me They wouldn't take me seriously."

He had been a manager of a small factory before the war, was a good talker and could deal with the lawyers better than me. The post office was still operating in the town, and they had good records in the Town Hall which would be a big help. Now we had to wait and see how things developed. We would let people know if they had a problem we would listen to their story. During the War of Independence and the Civil War large country estates had been attacked and the country houses burned. The people that owned them had been 'The Gentry' or old ruling class. Most of them left to go back to England and had become absentee landlords they had used agents to run the estates. Some of these agents were now occupying these properties. It was going to be difficult sorting out who owned what. I would need lots of help from the town committee. There was a lot of cattle rustling and stealing of livestock going on a state of lawlessness existed in some rural areas and this is what we were to try to eliminate.

Once we got set up, we started getting information of illegal land grabs, the committee would look up the deeds and then would recommend what should happen. I would then send troops to investigate these incidents which caused friction within the community as someone was always on the losing side. We were never going to be the most popular people in the area. 'Staters' was a word we frequently heard in a derogatory manner. We also had to collect taxes and land rents which were due to the Government. Again, this was another cause of resentment among the local people.

The strain on the troops began to tell and before very long problems arose, and it was hard to maintain discipline. The irregular forces used these circumstances for their own purposes to try and turn people against the

Provisional Government. We got a call from a farmer with a substantial farm saying that he had been threatened with violence if he didn't hand over some of his land. We went out to his farm and confronted some locals who thought they had a claim to this property.

"Who sent for you lot?" Asked this man.

"The owner requested our assistance," I answered.

"It's not his property, it belongs to the people," the man shouted.

"It was stolen by British and given to them," another man shouted.

"They're English," he said.

"When did all this happen?" I asked.

"I don't know, a long time ago," he answered.

"Well, it just so happens that Mr Crawford has a deed saying he owns this farm, and it has been run by his family for years, unless you can give me proof of your claim this family stays on the land, any more problems out here we will arrest the lot of you! It would answer you better to work the land you have and not try to take what is not yours. Go back to your homes," I said.

These types of incidents became commonplace, if it wasn't land it was stealing cattle or sheep. My men became tired of listening to claims of who is right or wrong and sometimes the shouting escalated to physical violence. Soldiers do not make good policemen; we are trained to fight not negotiate. We had several instances of my men getting into fights in the pubs in the town. I had to charge some of my own men for misconduct fighting and drunkenness. It was a no-win situation we did the best we could and in time helped to bring some kind of order to the general population.

On May 24th, 1923, Frank Aiken, now commanding the irregular forces, gave orders for his men to dump arms and return home. Although this was not an official surrender it did bring an end to hostilities. After almost a year the Civil War was over. By this time the stress of day to day dealing in what were essentially civic disputes was taking a toll on our morale, it was good news when we were told we would be relieved by another battalion. We would spend the next few weeks in Athlone barracks.

My wife Kate gave birth to another baby girl in June. I travelled down to Dublin to see her. We named her Maureen; she was robust and fair where Betty was dark and small Little by little the country was returning to normal. An election was to be held in August which would give us an indication of how the country was doing. The result of the election brought some stability, the Pro

Treaty won by a larger majority giving the Government more control. While I was home on leave my brother, Christy, arrived back in Dublin, he had been with General Prout in the southeast working in intelligence. It was great to see him. Now that the war had ceased, he was to be sent to the Curragh for another assignment.

"Well now what do you think of the way things are now?" Christy asked.

"Fighting a war was bad enough but this business of being policemen is not exactly what I signed up for," I said.

"You are always in the middle, and someone always get the short end of the stick. I will be glad when the Garda get properly organised and take over. It's hard on the troops. Morale is low," I answered.

"How did you make out?" I asked.

"We saw some action down through Waterford and Tipperary, mostly hit and run. It wasn't as bad as Cork and Kerry, we still lost quite a few men. Thank God the worst is over. I can't wait to get back to normal," Christy said.

"I hear they are going to be reducing the size of the Army," I said.

"They won't need all the men now that the War is over. Rumour has it that some of the higher ups are not too happy," Christy said. "They say a lot of the officers from the old days are to be let go. We just have to wait and see."

I returned to Sligo town after a week's leave. Things had settled down a bit Comdt. Conroy came up to see how we were doing. He told me the Special Infantry group was going to be disbanded in the next few weeks. The new Irish police force Garda Siochana would be setting up a police barracks in the town and as soon as they came, we were to report back to the Curragh to be demobbed or reassigned.

"What do you think you will do, Sam?" He asked.

"I like being a soldier, but I will have to wait and see what happens."

"Well good luck. I will see you in the Curragh."

Chapter 30

Towards the end of October, the Garda had moved into Sligo town. We packed up all our gear and started our move to The Curragh. Once in the Curragh things moved fairly quickly. Our battalion was disbanded, other than senior NCO's and officers almost all of the men were demobbed. The Army was reducing very fast. All the Special Infantry Group was broken up. There was some resentment on our part as we thought we were not being treated with the respect we deserved, in cases similar to myself we had served to the best of our ability we'd had to learn to be soldiers in life-or-death circumstances without the benefit of proper training. Some of us had paid the ultimate price, others had spent time in prison. Now the higher ranks seemed to be having a power struggle to see who ended up in charge.

In the Curragh I was assigned to administrative duties, helping to sort out the men who were leaving. It was not the kind of duty that suited me I would have been better working training troops. Maybe I wasn't cut out for a peace time Army. As I said the was a lot of friction in the top ranks and some of our former comrades were rebelling against the regime. These men were being accused of Mutiny! mostly they were ex ASU and Squad members who felt they were being overlooked in favour of British ex-servicemen who had joined up.

This move was led by Paddy Daly and Liam Tobin. I had served most of my Army life with these men and I, in principle, agreed with their views. However, to me this was politics, and I didn't have much time for politicians. I preferred people who followed their own convictions. Losing Michael Collins and Arthur Griffith was in my opinion the worst thing that could have happened to our country. I think they would have done things differently. The new government took a completely different approach.

Christy arrived at the Curragh a month later; like me he was to be either demobbed or reassigned. It was great to have him around, plus we could visit our families as passes were no problem. I loved going home to Kate we were a proper little family now Betty was almost three and Maureen six months. While at home I could think about our future. I had started playing football again with lads at the Curragh it kept me fit and also took my mind off the Army situation. The more I thought about it the more I realised how much of my youth had passed me by. I was almost 20 years old and had spent so much time under stress during the past years, it might be time for a complete change of pace.

"What do you think Sam?" Christy asked one evening as we walked around the camp.

"How do you mean?" I answered.

"This business with the higher ups? It's a mess. I thought we were finished taking sides," I said.

"Yeah, I agree! I think some of these fellas are just feathering their own nests," Christy said.

"I am going to resign. I have had enough. Get back to a normal life."

"Kate and I were talking, and I think I might do the same," I said. I don't think a peace time Army is the place for me. "Ma said I could go into the market with her if I want to buying and selling fish. I might try that, if not, I can always go back plastering. What would you do Christy?"

Ah. "There's a few things I can do, you have a family and responsibility, so you have to be careful. It won't be long before we find out."

We both resigned our commissions on March 29th, 1924, and went back to civilian life.

Book 2

Chapter 1
May 1924, Civilian Life

Waking up for the first time as a civilian was quite a change from what I had been used to. Getting used to the sound of children and Kate looking after them was going to take getting used to after military life. I had been given my allowances, 200 pounds for my service on my discharge which made it easier at least we were ok for money till I decided what I was going to do. My mother had suggested that I might work with her in the Fish Market I could do the buying and deal with shops and restaurants that she dealt with.

I gave it a try and found that I was not cut out for collecting bills and dealing with customers I needed physical work, so I decided to go back working as a plasterer. Mam wasn't surprised when I told her. I approached Creedons, the firm I had started out with. I knew Jack Nolan who was the foreman I had worked with in the past. "Hello, Jack, do you remember me?" I asked.

"Yes, you were with us a few years ago, what have you been up to?" He asked.

"I've been in the Army. I have been out a few months and I am looking for work," I told him. "Well there's plenty of work for trades at the moment. You didn't finish your time here, did you?"

"No, I was in Kilmainham for a while," I answered.

"I see. The problem is I couldn't give you the full rate till I see what you can do. I'll tell you what, I will give you a start at 5th year rate for three months. If I'm happy with your work after that you will get full rate. What do you think?" Jack said.

"I think I could live with that," I said. "Right so, you can start tomorrow over in O'Connell Street, they are rebuilding the Gresham Hotel." At least I had a job to go to now.

Being back in work gave me a lift, the building trade gets into your blood and I got stuck in. Within a few weeks Jack Nolan approached me. "Glad to be back, Sam?," he asked.

"Yeah, I am enjoying the work," I said. "I tried office work, but it didn't suit me."

"Well, I have to say I am pleased with your work so I will recommend full pay from next week."

"Thanks a lot, I appreciate that. I won't let you down." When I got home that evening, I told Kate my good news she was delighted. "We should go out to celebrate," I said.

"See if your Mam can come over." When Kate's Mam arrived, we went out and had a great night. Walking home I met an old pal from football, Jimmy Duggan.

"How are ya Sam? Long time, no see," he said.

"Good, you?" I answered. "This is my wife, Kate."

"Nice to meet you missus," he said.

"Are you still playing for the Bendigo," I asked.

"Yes, still trying, are you playing at all?" Jimmy asked. "I am just out of the Army and only home a couple of months, still finding my feet," I said.

"We could use a full back if you want to give it a go. There's training on Monday night at 7.oo if you are interested, give it a go," he said as he left "Good night Missus."

Kate had been listening to our conversation, "You know Sam that might be a good idea. It would be good for you; it would help you to take your mind off all that stuff you've been through," she said. "Yeah, it would be good to meet some of my old pals. Christy used to play with him. I'll talk to Christy."

The next day I went over to see Christy at Ma's house. "How is it going Christy, what are you up to?" I asked.

"You know just getting used to being home," he answered. I told him, I met Jimmy Duggan the other night and he was saying Bendigo were looking for a full back. "Do you think I should go up and see them?"

"Sure, it would be a good start back for you they're not a bad side."

"Are you still going to work for Mam?" I asked. "Yes, for the time being it suits me while I decide what is best for me." Christy had already started back playing for Bohemians FC. And was enjoying being back in the game.

The following Monday after work I cycled up to the Bendigo ground. I met Jimmy and he introduced me to the coach. "Jimmy tells me you are a useful full back; we are looking for some new players. If you would like to you can join in our training?"

"Yeah, I would," I answered. I got changed and started training. Running sprints, heading the ball and then a five aside game was great. It felt good to be back on the pitch with a purpose. After the training, the coach came over to me and said, "You are in good shape just need to get your game timing right so if you want you can come and play with us. I will put you in the reserve team first, what do you think?"

"That's fine with me," I said.

"Ok next Saturday here at 3 o'clock."

"Thanks, I'll see you then." I cycled home excited to tell Kate I was going to start playing football again. As soon as I got in the door, "Well how did you get on?" Kate asked.

"I am starting in the reserve team on Saturday."

Kate gave me a hug, "well you better get your rest," she said.

"Are the kids asleep?" I asked smiling.

"Yes, they are asleep."

"Ok we better lie down so I can get my rest," I said leading her to the bed.

The next few weeks passed by quickly, I started playing with the Bendigo. I enjoyed being back on the field competing, between working, training and helping Kate with the girls I hadn't time to dwell on anything but the present. Little by little the horrors of the Civil War became a distant memory. Christy came over to our house one evening all excited. "You won't believe what I am going to be doing," he said.

"What do you mean?" I asked. "I am going to play football for Ireland in the Olympics in Paris."

"Whose leg do you think you are pulling are you joking me?" I asked.

"No seriously they were looking to send a team and I was picked to go," Christy said.

"How did you manage that?" I asked.

"Well first you have to be an amateur, then you need the time. Two weeks away and you have to pay your own travel expenses. I still have the grant we got when we were discharged. Oh! and you have to be good enough to play! There's five players from Boh's 5 from the Gate and 5 from Athlone town and 1 from

Brooklynn. We play at least two games. We leave on the 24th of May and play our first game on the 28th against Bulgaria."

"That's fantastic I am jealous, you will be the first men ever to play for the Irish Free State. Congratulations!" I said wishing him well.

Chapter 2
1924 Olympics

I brought Betty and Maureen out on the train to Dun Laoghaire to watch Christy and his teammates set off on their journey to Hollyhead the excitement was palpable. We gave them a big wave as the steamer cast off and they began their adventure.

Christy and the team caught the boat from Dun Laoghaire to Hollyhead. There were 16 players and several officials and our own trainers and coach. It would be a long gruelling journey by boat ,train and ferry to Calais in France, then another train to Paris. We would be the first athletes to represent Ireland in an Olympic games. For most of us it was also our first time out of Ireland, what an exciting time. We travelled through Wales across England down to Dover where we caught a ferry to Calais in France.

Although a tiring journey it was exciting knowing we were going to the Olympic Games. Then we went by train to Paris. I was amazed to see Paris such an airy and cosmopolitan city compared to Dublin which was still partly in ruins from the war. We stayed at a hotel in the city close to where we would be playing. Paddy Harris was our trainer and coach; he held a similar job at Bohemians. We had only one training session before our game with Bulgaria. I wasn't picked to make the team for the first game as we had more experienced players than me. The game was played in a huge stadium, The Stade de France in Paris, there were very few spectators, as the football tournament was being held before the other games were to begin and we did not get the publicity to draw bigger crowds.

And so, on 28th of May 1924 we began our quest as Irelands footballing heroes. We played in a blue jersey with white shorts and black socks with blue trim. The badge was white with a green shamrock on it. The Bulgarians wore green. The stadium was very hot, and our lads battled against a very dogged Bulgarian team hitting the woodwork 3 times in the first half. In the second half it took till the 75th minute for a great strike from Paddy Duncan of James Gate to score our first international goal which won us the game and set us up for a game against Holland in the next round. We were overjoyed to think we had won our first international game.

On Monday the 2nd of June again we took to the field in the Stade de France . It was a fantastic stadium which could hold up to 80,000 people. These first games were not well attended which was sad. Again, I had the disappointment of missing out on playing against Holland, but that's football. Ireland put up a great fight against the Dutchmen coming back from a goal scored against us in the 8th minute. Frank Ghent scored in the second half to bring us level and force overtime. The extra time was a battle with the Dutch finally scoring, beating us 2 to 1 in a hard-fought victory. Although we lost, we could hold our heads high, and we were proud of our performance.

I finally got my chance to play a couple of days later against Estonia on June 4th. There were four new players in this team, 3 of us from Boh's and 1 from the Gate. It's hard to explain what it felt like to line out for your country in an International Match. I felt very proud. The game was close for the first 15 minutes then we began to find our feet and began to make some good passes. I got the ball from John Joe Dykes the captain that day and took off down the line and crossed a ball into the box. Where John Thomas one of my teammates from Boh's jumped and scored our first goal with a great header.

I was up and down the pitch enjoying myself the grass was perfect making it easy to control the ball. The full back was a tough defender and let me know I was not going to have it all my own way. He brushed me aside going for a ball and caught me with his elbow for good measure. Being small I could turn quickly and used this to my advantage making him a little frustrated. Now with our nerves settled we began to enjoy ourselves passing the ball with accuracy. Just after half time Tommy Muldoon got a fine pass from John Thomas and scored.

I received a ball from a goal kick and headed for the penalty area only to be cut down by the centre half. The next time I got the ball I knew I would have to be quick to get by him. I faked a shot which caused him to shift the wrong way and I slipped by him putting myself in a shooting position. I steadied myself and fired a low shot off my right foot to the corner of the goal beating the goalie. What a feeling seeing the ball enter the goal from my boot. The first goal I ever scored for my country. Estonia got a goal before the end, and we ended up winning 3 to 1.

We had done ourselves proud. That evening a Parisian football Club with strong Irish connections Cercle Athletique held a reception for us. Jules Rimet president of FIFA was in attendance who was later to organise the first World Cup in 1932 and in who's honour the World Cup Trophy was named. We had a brilliant evening ended with a lusty rendition on The Soldiers Song.

We spent a couple of days seeing the sights and delights of Paris. The Roaring Twenties were in full swing taking hold in Paris and coming from Dublin we had only begun to emerge from the Victorian era. We were used to women with long dresses down to their ankles and black seemed to be their favourite colour. Here in Paris the girls wore short skirts and colourful clothes. The warm weather also meant they didn't wear coats. So many pretty girls walking around made for great entertainment and we certainly enjoyed it.

There was buzz about the city brought on by the Olympic spirit and so many visitors it was great atmosphere. We even went to see the Follies which we couldn't tell our mothers about. We had to balance this with a visit to Notre Dame cathedral. It was quite an eye-opening experience. All too soon we had to head home. It was a trip that I would never forget. I couldn't wait to tell Sam all about it.

On Saturday afternoon Sam went to meet Christy at the train station at Westland Row on his return, as he couldn't wait to hear all about Christy's experiences. There was a crowd waiting as the train pulled in, People started clapping and cheering as they arrived. We were proud of them as they had acquitted themselves well. There was a great atmosphere on the station platform with everyone greeting one another. I finally saw Christy and hugged him. "welcome home brother how did you get on?" I asked.

"It was brilliant," Christy answered.

"Yes, I was reading about you in the papers they gave you a good write up. Too bad you didn't get by Holland," Sam said.

"If we had been together a little longer, I think we could have beat them, the heat was tough," Christy said. "What a great city it was magnificent, the football was pretty good too," he answered. "We had a great time and the French people treated us very well. We gave a good account of ourselves the Dutch team only beat us in extra time, and they were beaten by the eventual winners."

"Your name was in the paper. I see you scored against Estonia," I said. "Yes, we won well I would have loved to be in against the Dutch I would have liked a go at their full back he wasn't the quickest, maybe next time," Christy said as we got a tram home to Ma's house. Christy had little gift's for all of us, keepsakes from Paris.

The USA football that had travelled to Paris made a special stop in Dublin on their way home, to play against The Irish Free State giving us international standing. The game was played in a packed Dalymount in front of 30,000 fans. Some new players were added to the team men who had been unable to go to Paris. I was picked to play; we had a new player Ned Brooks who made history by scoring all 3 goals in a 3 to 0 win for over the US. I was delighted to play as it was my home ground and my family was able to come and watch what a proud moment for me. It was great for the fans to witness the first international game of the Irish Free State.

The excitement of Christy's adventure stayed with me, and I was determined to improve my fitness and ability as a footballer so I might one day get the chance to play for my country. One evening after I got back from work Kate was in an anxious mood. "What's wrong?" I asked.

"Betty hasn't been well all day, she has had a hard time getting her breath," she said.

"I'll take her up to the hospital and get her checked out right away," I said. I got on my bike with Betty on the cross bar and headed for Temple St Children's Hospital. They took her in right away to examine her. She was listless and very pale and was struggling to breath. The doctor told me she had had an asthma attack and started giving her some oxygen and medicine to help her to breath. He also noticed that her spine was crooked, and she was developing a hump on her back. They were going to keep her in the hospital for a few days to get her breathing properly and would do some tests to see what they could do to help.

She was now 4 years old and she didn't like the idea of staying in the hospital. This would be the first of many visits to the hospital in the future. Betty would be diagnosed with acute asthma and would suffer with this complaint all her life. Now with two girls to look after Kate was again pregnant, life was pretty busy for us.

Chapter 3
Bohemians

In 1926 I bought myself a second-hand motorcycle with a side car. It was a Norton 450. A friend of mine had owned it and now had got himself a car. In the Army I had occasion to ride motorcycles which I really enjoyed so when the opportunity came, I jumped at it. We still had two little girls as Kate had lost the other baby which was stillborn. Kate was feeling bad with the loss of the baby and I hoped us having the motor bike would help lift her spirits. We would be able to go on picnics and jaunts through the countryside with the children. I was excited as I rode it home from my friend's house. I rode up and parked outside our house on Mountjoy Street.

I knocked on the door and when Kate answered I brought her and the girls out to see my new pride and joy. I hadn't mentioned that I would be getting a bike, so it came as a complete surprise to Kate. "Well, what do you think do you like it?" I asked.

"Where did you get it?" Kate asked.

"A friend was selling it and I thought it would be nice to have our own transport especially in the summer," I answered.

"Plus, the price was right. The girls jumped into the side car."

Maureen said, "Daddy let's go."

"It's lovely," Kate said with a smile. It was a nice bright evening. I said, "All jump in and we'll go show Uncle Christy."

"Get your coats and we will go," said Kate. With that the Robinsons piled in and we went for our first of many motorcycle rides. The kids and Kate loved it.

Mam's business was doing much better now with the stability in the country. My sister Molly had married Mark and they also now had three children with the growing family my mother had bought a house up in Glasnevin on Mobhi Rd. and had moved in with Dinah, Molly and her family. Just on the other side of the

Royal Canal outside the city, it was one of Dublin's new suburbs. Although you could walk to the city centre in 15 minutes, it felt like the country.

I had been playing in the first team at Bendigo in the Leinster League now for more than a year, when Ex Col. Dalton showed up at one of our games. After the game which we won well against Athlone Town he sought me out. "How are you, Sam?" He asked.

"Doing great, Sir," I said.

"It's not Sir any more just plain old Joe. I am with Bohemians and I was wondering if you would like to come and play with us. We have been watching you and we think you would fit in very well with us. We are building a strong team and we need some new players. Your brother Christy is in our team as you know, and I think in this new league we need more players. You know we are still an amateur club so it's tough against the pros. What do you think?" Asked Col. Dalton.

"I'd love to play with Bohs," I answered. "Come up to Dalymount Park tomorrow and we will sort out the paperwork. I have already spoken with your coach and he understands the situation." The following day I walked up to Dalymount Park and signed on to be a player for Bohemians F.C. I had reached a high in my footballing career.

Bohemians were the glamour team in Dublin in 1926. They were known as 'The Gypsies' and had a great reputation. The Team had been founded by students in the 1890's and they had progressed through the different leagues to become a great organisation and a respected football team who had produced some of Ireland's best footballers. Some of my former Army associates were involved with Boh's. The Dalton brothers who were committee members. I started off again playing in the reserve team and would have to wait my turn to play in the first team. Playing in Dalymount was great it was the biggest ground in the league. Any big games, Cup finals etc. were held there. It had been donated by a lord who owned it, he rented it to Boh's for one pound a year as long as Boh's remained an amateur team.

I got my opportunity a few months later when one of the full backs in the senior team was injured. I got to play against Drumcondra in my first game. I was a bit nervous when we walked out on the field for the first time. The Capt. Harry Cannon a veteran goalkeeper told me not to worry just play your own game. Once the game started, I began to relax and started to play. The level of skill in this team compared to Bendigo was much higher.

The passing was faster, and you had to be on your toes to keep up with the play. Also, most of the teams in the top division were professional and the game is much more physical you need to be strong and tough. The inside forward I was marking went up to head a ball and gave me an elbow in the face as he landed. He carried on as if nothing happened, I took his number. The tackles were hard and sometimes left their marks. The team played very well, and we soon had a two-goal lead with Jimmy White scoring both. Christy was out on the right side and I managed to give him a couple of long passes which made me feel good. It was a much more physical game against professional players. They had all kinds of tricks pulling jersey 's clipping your heels they were also very fit strong and moved fast, and I had to be at my best to match their speed. In the end we finished winning 3 to 1.

With my first game behind me I went into the dressing room with a good feeling. "You did all right out there," Harry Cannon said. This was the start of a great adventure which I would relish. I began to play regularly in the first team and started to make the full back position my own. The team slowly began to blossom, and we were very hard to beat. Playing football rearing a young family and working was a great way of regaining my youth which I had lost during the troubles and the Civil War. All of my teenage years had been spent in the fighting for my country, I was now the ripe old age of 23. I was enjoying my life. In 1926, I won my first medal with the team as we won the Leinster Senior Cup. This was the beginning of a period where Bohemians dominated League of Ireland football.

Football in Dublin was very popular we would get big crowds at Dalymount on Saturday or Sunday, it wasn't long before I would be recognised walking down the street by people I didn't even know. It felt good when someone gave you a compliment or bid you the time of day, recognising your efforts on the football field. We now had three children Kate had given birth to our third child, another baby girl, Kathleen. With three children our flat in Mountjoy Street was getting too small. We would have to find a bigger place. I had been talking to Ma about it when she said she may have a solution. There was a house for sale in Little Mary Street she had her eye on and it might suit us. "Ma I don't think I could afford to buy a house like that," I said.

"Well, you are going to have to do something. I might be able to help," she said. "Christy could stay with you and help with the expense also. Do you not have any of your army money left?"

"I have a few bob left, about 50 quid," I said. "I can sell the motorbike. It's too small now with the kids, I should get 30 quid for it."

"Between us we can come up with what we need." Ever the businesswoman Mam made things happen. Between us all somehow, Christy ended up with the motorbike, we managed to get the deposit and bought number 25 Little Mary Street. It was a three-storey house with a shop on the ground floor which would become our family home for the next 25 years.

The season of 1927/1928 became the ultimate season of football for Boh's. I was now a trusted part of the team and I played both as a full back and sometimes as a half back. We had developed into a cohesive unit that played with flair and tenacity. Christy and the other forwards provided the flair while myself and the other defenders were the steel in defence. When playing I became a different person, my competitive instinct took over and I was ruthless and knew no fear.

Often while playing I could anticipate the run of a forward and get my tackle in taking man and ball if necessary. I developed into a feared defender often called that 'black bastard' owing to my dark complexion and black hair. The Team of 1927/28 became a great team led by the Captain Harry Cannon the goalkeeper and the likes of Billy Dennis, Johnny McIlroy, Jimmy Birmingham etc. We were so confident, we felt we could beat anybody. We were flying high everything going our way.

After winning a semi-final game against Athlone town we were all in great spirits in the dressing room. As usual the team were in high spirits and we were clowning around. I was walking past the players to go to the shower, when one of our lads swung a towel at me which I ducked. In doing so I upset a large bucket of boiling water, it fell to the floor and splashed all over my right leg and torso. I was scalded badly.

The trainer started work on me right away getting me into the cold shower and spraying the areas that were hurt. My leg was badly damaged, and the pain was awful. The team doctor Willie Hooper was sent for and he treated me in the dressing room. He covered my leg with my famous Zambuk ointment and applied dressings. We had three weeks to the final against our biggest rivals Shamrock Rovers. Kate was very upset when I arrived home by taxi this was the first time anything like this had happened to me. It took all the care from Kate and the doctor to enable me to play in the final. Leg was bound up tight for the game and it was touch and go whether I would be fit enough to play.

It was a close-run thing, and in the end, we beat Rovers 1- 0 in a very tough match. Giving us a clean sweep of all the trophies in Ireland. However, the consequence of the scalding left me with scar tissue on my shin and leg that caused me a lot of trouble all my adult life. At the end of that season a game was arranged between Belfast Celtic, the champions of Northern Ireland, and Bohemians for bagging rights as the best team in Ireland. A full capacity of over 30,000 people showed up at Dalymount to watch the game. It was a fantastic game with all the drama of a cup final. Both goals led a charmed life with goalies at full stretch to save shots.

I was playing right half and towards the last 10 minutes found myself with the ball just over the halfway line. Johnny McMahon was inside me; I pushed the ball to him and took off at a run down the touch line Johnny chipped the ball over the full back and I had a clear run at it. As I reached the ball I looked up and Jimmy McIlroy was running into the box. I fired the ball over the goalie who flailed at it. The ball sailed over him and Jimmy headed a beautiful shot past him into the net. What a feeling seeing that ball nestle in the net. We were now without a doubt the Best team in Ireland.

Chapter 4
International Footballer

Life was good, playing football, having moved into our own house and still working as a plasterer. Kate and the children were happy in their new surroundings. The only problem we seemed to have was, Betty's asthma had gotten worse, and her schooling was suffering. Betty was a very intelligent child as a seven-year-old, was bright and could read well beyond her age limit. Her hump on her back also became more noticeable which caused her some embarrassment. She was still determined to attend school and went as much as was possible.

I had to on several occasions bring her to the Gas Company works in Irishtown so she could inhale some of the sulphur smell that we were told the fumes would help her. Wise beyond her years with the face of a little Madonna she would always hold a special place in my heart. My first son was born in February 1927, we named him Charlie after my father, a small little fella with jet black hair and a dark complexion, Kate at last had a son to dote on.

I returned from work one evening to find a letter waiting for me. "Who's the letter from?" asked Kate. "It's from The Irish Free State Football Association. I have been selected to the International team to play against Belgium!"

"My God that's fantastic. I am so proud of you," said Kate. "When is this?"

"I have to check. It said it will be a three-week trip. I'll have to check with work," I said.

"Surely that won't be a problem," Kate said.

"I hope not," I answered. Needless to say, I was over the moon getting my chance to play for my country. It was such an honour. "I am going to run down to Ma's and tell her, she will be delighted," I said.

"Can I come with you Daddy?" Betty asked.

"Of course, you can," I answered.

"Me too," said Maureen. I tucked the two of them on to my bicycle and set of for Mobhi Rd. Christy was at my Ma's when we arrived. Dinah answered the door delighted to see the girls. "What brings you over here this evening?" She asked.

"I got some good news I thought you would like to hear," I said. I walked into the kitchen Mam was sitting by the fireplace in her usual chair.

"Well, this is a nice surprise," she said. Mam, Molly and Christy were at the table having their tea.

"I just got picked to play for Ireland against Belgium," I blurted out, "the game is going to be played in Belgium."

"That's great!" Christy said.

"When's the game?" He asked.

"It's in February," I answered.

"You will love it," said Christy, "well done you deserve it." When I play, I will have achieved the same accolades as my big brother.

I approached my boss at work about the fact that I would need two weeks off in order to travel with the Irish team. 'Jack Nolan my foreman was a decent man to work for and had treated me well since my return. It was now January and I had to go in early February. "Can I have a word Jack?" I asked.

"Sure, what's up?" he asked.

"I have been picked to play for Ireland in Belgium next month."

"Congratulations, that's great," he said. "The thing is I need two weeks off; we are travelling over to Belgium."

"Oh, that might be a problem! You know it's not up to me. I will have to talk to the bosses and see what they say. I'll get back to you." The next day Jack spoke with me. "I spoke with my boss he said you can have the time off without pay. There is no guarantee we can keep your job open, if we have to get jobs finished."

"I understand," I said keeping my feelings to myself. Just imagine playing for your country and being treated like this.

"You know it's not the way I would do things if it was up to me," Jack said.

"Yeah, I know that. Thanks Jack," I said. The Irish Free State was still not acceptable to some people. Politics!

There were five Bohemian players including myself picked for the Irish team. Harry Cannon, Jack McCarthy, Capt. Jimmy White and Jack Sullivan. We set off on our long journey; we took the mail boat to Holyhead and then a train to Dover. Then a ferry to Calais and then a train into Belgium. It was my first time to travel out of Ireland and I was so excited. What an experience travelling through countries where only a few years before World War 1 had raged. Ruined landscapes still remained and there were scars visible as the train rushed through the countryside of northern France.

Our game was to be held in the City of Liege. We received a warm welcome in Liege, we stayed at a lovely hotel and were able to explore the city. A training ground was arranged, and we started to train. We had some new players and we had to get used to one another.

The game was held in the Stade Maurice Dufranse in Liege Belgium. There was a capacity crowd of 35,000 the largest crowd we ever played in front of. Lining out in a green Jersey for the first time was special a feeling that I will never forget. Belgium had a strong and physical team it wasn't long before we knew we were in a game. Harry Cannon was called on to make a save within a couple of minutes. One of their forwards, Jean Diddens, was a flyer and crossed the ball into the box where the centre forward headed towards our goal and caught the corner in the 38th minute. We went 1 down. No sooner had the game restarted when one of their star players, Francois Ledent, scored with a great volley from the edge of the box.

Going in at half time 2 goals down was tough. Jack McCarthy and Harry Cannon gave us both barrels in the dressing room. "Don't forget who you are, they are good but so are we! Tighten up the defence and inside forwards come back and help the backs and let's have a go at these fellas. Get stuck into them."

The second half started, and we came out with renewed energy. Diddens came down the wing with the ball at his feet as he got ready to cross, I came across and slid in taking the ball and him into touch. He backed off then, he didn't like being tackled. It was our throw and Jack Sullivan got the ball out to Jimmy White who beat the centre half and smashed the ball into the top corner. 2 to 1 before they could get organised. Jack McCarthy got a ball from Paddy Barry and slid it to Billy Lacey who dribbled past the full back and beat the goalie low at the post. They were now nervous and started making mistakes. We got a corner in the 73rd minute and Jimmy White made sure heading it past the goalie.

In the 77th minute Jack McCarthy and Jimmy White were making a nuisance of themselves in the penalty box, White was chopped down by the full back winning us a penalty. Jack Sullivan stepped up and score. We won 4 to 2. What a feeling we could hardly believe it. My first international and a winner. That night a great time was had by all we found a local bar and sang and drank the night away.

I had made my debut in international football and I was feeling good. The people of Belgium had been gracious in defeat and gave us some applause as we left the field. Before we left, I made my way to the shopping area of Liege. I had never bought a proper engagement ring for Kate. So, I thought I might be able to get something nice for her. I found a jewellery shop and bought a lovely ring with lovely red stones which I felt she would like; it would always be a reminder of my time in Liege. We didn't feel the long journey home as we were on a high after our first win.

Kate was delighted with the ring which she cherished all her life. On my return I was approached by a new team, Dolphins, who were a professional team playing out of Dolphins Barn. They had a lot of international players, playing for them and wanted me to sign on. With my growing family the opportunity to earn extra money was a decision I would wrestle with. I approached this dilemma by talking to Christy who always had my best interest at heart. "What do you think?" I asked.

"If I was in your position with a young family, I would go to Dolphins you have given your all to Boh's. It's about time you got something more than glory out of the game, it won't last forever." With that advice I decided to sign with Dolphins. I started playing in the 1930/31 season.

Chapter 5
Dolphins F.C.

Being a professional footballer in Dublin in the 1930's was not what it is today. I still remained working as a plasterer being my day job. I trained 3 evenings a week and we played mostly on the weekend with the occasional game through the week. I got paid a weekly fee, four pounds a week, and sometimes we were paid bonuses if we won cup games. The extra income was welcome as I was paying a mortgage on our house and had 4 children and a pregnant wife. But life was good, I was doing what I loved to do and was getting well paid for it. The team were all highly skilled players who were a joy to play with. We had some of the best players in Ireland and a couple of players from Scotland playing with us.

It was great to play with the famous Alex Stevenson a crafty wizard of a winger who was worshipped. It was a heady time in the new Free State Football Association, football was popular, and we drew large crowds who watched us play. The ritual of Saturday or Sunday out at a game and then a pint at your local with all the banter involved by supporters was a necessary outlet for the working man in Dublin which was still struggling with unemployment and immense poverty in certain areas. Families on the whole were large and lived barely above the poverty line. I enjoyed playing for Dolphins, the only thing I missed was Dalymount park.

In 1931 I was again picked to play for my country, I was to be part of a team to play Spain in Barcelona. Again, this would entail weeks away from work and family. I was now working for a building company called Fearon's who had their own football team and had no trouble getting the time off. I would eventually play with them when my professional career ended. The excitement around the house when I announced that I was going to Spain was fantastic. It was such an exotic destination. "Daddy it's very warm in Spain," I was told by Maureen, "and they have oranges on the trees."

"How would you know about oranges?" I asked.

"Betty told me; she knows everything."

"They were looking at an Atlas to see where Spain was when they heard you were going," Kate told me. "It had a picture of orange trees."

"Too bad we couldn't all go," I said. "Maybe, someday."

We again started out on our journey travelling by ship to England and then by train down to Dover and across the English Channel to France. We then took a train all down through France into the Pyrenees and the into Spain. The journey although tiring was magnificent the different landscapes and the change from green fields in France to the huge mountains of Spain and the dry arid plains as we made our way south to Barcelona. None of us had ever been this far away from home before and we were fascinated to experience the different culture and country. Descending from the mountains into the plain where Barcelona lay gave our first us glimpses of the blue Mediterranean Sea and the Basque Country.

Barcelona was a beautiful city with wide streets and bright coloured buildings. It was also located on the Mediterranean with beautiful beaches not far from the city. Our hotel was within easy reach of the sea which for me was a bonus as I am an avid sea swimmer. Our team had a few new players with us on this trip most notably Paddy Moore of Shamrock Rovers, a brilliant footballer and prolific goal scorer, whom I had the occasional tousle with on the pitch. I was looking forward to being on the same side for a change. We had a couple of days to get ready for the game.

So, I enjoyed swimming in the warm waters of the Med. The people of Barcelona gave us a warm reception we got to see the wonderful sights of the city we even saw a bull fight which was gory but fascinating. We had to get used to the heat during the day the temperature was almost 80 degrees. Plus, we were used to a heavy wet ball here the ball seemed much lighter. We had a couple of training session before the game to get us ready.

On game day we were bussed to the Stadium, when I say Stadium, we could not believe the size of it. In Liege the ground held 35,000 this place could hold 100,000, it was enormous. Walking out onto the field which was like a huge billiard table. Manicured to perfection, it is hard to describe. What a place to play football. It was what I thought the Coliseum in Rome would have looked like to the Gladiators. There was an echo as we knocked the ball around before any fans arrived. We went to the dressing rooms to prepare. Every facility was available, tables for massage, ice cold baths and hot showers. It was comparable to a fine hotel. Our training staff worked on us and when we walked out to play, we were ready.

The Spanish team were led by their goalkeeper and captain Zamora who was reckoned to be one of the best in the world. They also had a budding superstar Sanchez, a winger of great speed and ability. I would have my work cut out for me today as I was playing right full back. I had Jack McCarthy as centre half and Harry Cannon in goal. We were a strong and physical side and with Moore up front alongside Jimmy White we could be a threat.

When we walked out from under the stand all we could see was a sea of people the whole ground was full. There were drums beating and Spanish flags all over the stands. "Talk about intimidation." We stood as they played the anthems and then gathered around in a circle before the kick-off. Jack McCarthy spoke, "There's only 11 of them and 11 of us, so let's show them what we are made of." Wearing the Green jersey is a privilege, and we would conduct ourselves to the best of our ability. Way up in one of the stands there was a small Tricolour; it gave us strength.

As the game got under way the Spaniards began passing the ball around with confidence. "Come on lads get stuck into these fellas," Harry Cannon roared. We reacted with tackles that showed them we were not overawed by their fancy footwork. The centre forward got a ball and headed for our goal. Jack made a fierce tackle and took the ball away, the Spaniard feeling the brunt of the tackle. Clearing the ball to Jimmy White who flashed a pass to Moore who let fly missing the net.

A warning to the Spanish we do not lie down. The heat was a problem we had to deal with also the noise made by the crowd was incredible. When they strung a few passes together the crowd would start 'Ole' with each pass made. Sanchez the winger was running me every time he got the ball. He was brilliant and I had to use every trick I knew to keep him at bay. Being small he could turn on a sixpence and you couldn't take your eyes off him. They got a corner from the left side that should have scored but hit the bar. Then just before half time they scored with a great pass through the middle from Sanchez that their centre forward blasted into our goal.

At half time we looked drained, the heat getting to us. The training staff to their credit worked wonders to get us out for the second half. Once on the field we felt we could compete with these lads. Although our goal led a charmed life with Cannon making a couple of great saves. As the game went on, we were able to hold our own and Paddy Moore began to show why he was regarded the best forward in Ireland. He jinked though their defence a couple of times causing panic in the back line only to be caught offside.

Then Harry Cannon caught a ball in our box, he booted it out to Jimmy White who slipped the ball to our winger Kinsella. He took off down the line and crossed before the full back reached him. The ball bounced near the penalty box and running in was Paddy Moore who volleyed it past Zamora to score. The crowd was stunned into silence. We then had to weather a storm as they came at us, I was never so glad to hear the final whistle. We were completely spent I could hardly walk off the pitch.

What an achievement. the crowd gave us a great ovation as we walked off. They appreciated the effort we had given. I had earned my second international cap. Playing against Spain in such a magnificent Stadium was a thrilling experience. No one would have given us a chance against Spain, and we came away with a draw.

On the way back to Dublin we stopped at the town of Lourdes across the Spanish border in France. This is where the Virgin Mary had appeared to Saint Bernadette. It was already a special place with lots of visitors on pilgrimage here. It was ideal for a quick visit and it also gave us a break and a chance to get to know each other better.

Once back in Dublin it was almost summer and there would not be any football for a while. I was back working as a plasterer for Fearon's. Between Christy and I we had rented a house in Skerries for two weeks for our summer holidays. Skerries was a seaside town located about twenty miles north of Dublin on the coast. The house we rented was across from the harbour and had a lovely beach. The first two weeks in August were our holidays, we took the train to Skerries with all the children. Christy had brought his motorcycle and he rode down with his girlfriend Margaret.

It was a great adventure for our family as we had never been away like this before. The kids were delighted with the beach across the road. Betty thrived away from the polluted city air and although not able to keep up physically with the others still was the boss and organiser for the others. It was quite a change for the children running around carefree, Kate was again expecting a baby in

November and was content to sit and watch the carry on as we swam and wrestled and played by the seashore.

We enjoyed the sunshine and the tranquillity of a perfect summer. Like all good things it was over before we knew, and we would soon return to our house in Little Mary Street. Our newest child was born that November, a boy. We called him Jeremiah, he was not in the best of health and only lived for three weeks. It was a sad time for us, especially Kate. A child being stillborn had been bad enough, now to see your baby perish only weeks old was devastating for her. I alone brought the baby in a small white coffin to the angel's plot in Glasnevin and he was buried there with a lot of other unfortunate children.

This was probably the hardest blow our family had so far suffered. We again were to feel the loss of a child when another of our children a 14-month-old girl Eileen died of pneumonia a couple of years later. Our family was not unique in this as conditions in Dublin were hard, the city was badly polluted and conditions poor in a lot of the tenements. were ravaged with lung disease and TB.

By 1935, my football career was coming to a close. Dolphins Football Club were having financial problems and were stepping down from the League of Ireland. My leg that had been badly scalded was also giving me trouble. I needed constant care on my shin on my left leg as the scalding had reduced the thickness of the skin which became infected if I got a bad knock. So, in 1935 I decided to quit playing as a professional footballer. Working for Fearon's I would still play on occasion with their team. This was just to keep fit and for the enjoyment of being part of a team.

Our family was now six, with baby Phyllis being born that year. Betty, now 14 years old, had finished primary school. She had missed out on some of her schooling due to her illness but was amazing when it came to working with her hands. She was the most creative person of the family and could sew or knit better than most grown women. We continued to live in Little Mary Street and with a growing family, it took all my time working to look after them. Then the world changed within a few years and with another World War looming, I would again, in 1939, wear the green uniform of an Irish soldier.

The End